The
HEALING
POWER
Of
AYAHUASCA

16 Incredible Life Transformations
That Will Inspire Your Self-Discovery

By

Marc McLean

Free Audio Download For You

Hear the first-hand accounts of 10 of the people interviewed in this book as they talk about their magical experiences with ayahuasca.

Author Marc McLean has pulled together snippets from the recorded interviews he did with the men and women sharing their stories in *The Healing Power Of Ayahuasca*.

Hear their voices as they speak openly about their ayahuasca journeys, their biggest lessons they learned from drinking the plant medicine, and their advice for readers like you.

You can download the audio recording online by visiting: **www.healingpowerofaya.com/audio**

The Healing Power Of Ayahuasca

16 Incredible Life Transformations That Will Inspire Your Self-Discovery

Table of Contents

INTRODUCTION

∽

"The answers are within," said some wise person.

But how do we actually go inside ourselves to find the answers to our problems?

Who can show us how to heal when Western medicine has failed time after time? Who can hand us the key to our padlocked subconscious mind so we can see what's really going on in there, and then break our destructive patterns? Which genius can help us properly understand why life seems to be one long, repetitive mess at times?

Mother can: 'Mother Ayahuasca'.

I don't know exactly why you picked up this book. Maybe ayahuasca has randomly come into your life - like it did for me - or maybe you simply read the words 'healing power' in the title and felt drawn to learning more about this miraculous plant medicine. Who knows?

What I do know is that when life gets painful we go searching. Searching for ways to overcome the depression, break the addiction, fix the relationship, heal the chronic health problem, or simply to figure out why you've always felt that something's 'just not right'.

You might take the prescribed pills, join a weekly support group, get into fitness, meditation, the law of attraction, go vegetarian, then vegan, get a job promotion, move house, move onto yet another relationship, find a new obsession, then another…always looking for solutions that are 'out there'.

Those answers are inside ourselves and we've got no hope of finding them with traditional Western medicine where symptoms are masked, emotions are numbed, and we never properly heal the root causes of our problems.

This book shares 16 incredible stories of people who instead turned to the plant medicine ayahuasca, an alternative healing method that's been used for thousands of years. A method effectively used by indigenous tribes in the Amazon jungle that guides people on an inner journey where they can finally access - and heal - what's hurting them most.

In this book you'll learn about the amazing healing power of ayahuasca for all sorts of emotional, psychological and even physical issues.

Questions or doubts you may have had about this mystical, magical plant medicine will be answered in this collection of incredible first-hand accounts.

You'll be inspired that you too can overcome your darkest days with the help of ayahuasca, just like the people in this book who are now living healthier, happier lives.

You'll be given hope that you can become well again, even if doctors, therapists, or all other avenues of treatment have let you down in the past.

Ayahuasca is now gradually spreading far beyond the Amazon. The jungle medicine somehow reached me more than 6,000 miles away in Scotland in March 2017 after I had a complete meltdown. Emotionally, mentally, physically...I was a wreck. I'd hit the lowest point in my life.

I returned home from my ayahuasca retreat feeling like a completely new man. It physically felt like I'd been cleansed of decades worth of heavy, negative energy. I'd just been introduced to myself for the first time - and it was time to get to know the real me.

Ayahuasca shined a spotlight on my negative behaviours, repetitive mental patterns, and the ways in which I'd been making life difficult for myself. My subconscious mind was blasted wide open and I reached parts of myself that would be impossible to discover without plant medicine.

There aren't enough words to properly explain the powerful impact ayahuasca has had on my life…but I'll give it my best shot in chapter 16 of this book.

First, I'll share the incredible true stories of 15 other people from all over the world who have transformed their lives as a result of drinking ayahuasca. Brave people who were suffering and ayahuasca somehow appeared on their path to give them a way out.

An American woman who overcame bulimia and the depression that had haunted her from the age of 11.

A South African woman addicted to heroin for four years cured overnight.

An elderly Dutchman who discovered the medicine for the first time aged 85 - and released childhood trauma from the Second World War.

Just a few of the mindblowing stories the amazing people in this book have shared with me. It's an honour to share them with you.

I've been a journalist for the past 17 years and, while the media is admittedly filled with too many negative, fear-driven headlines, there was always one particular type of story that interested me most. The heroic tale of someone miraculously overcoming the toughest challenges life throws at them.

Ayahuasca is creating those kind of miracles every day. The plant medicine is guiding more and more people on an inner journey where they can become their own hero. It's giving people the power to heal themselves mentally, emotionally and physically, often when they have exhausted every other option.

The natives in the Amazon rainforest who faithfully use ayahuasca for healing say that Western society is broken. They tell us that all of our ills are down to losing our connection with spirit. They brew ayahuasca from two specific plants, the ayahuasca vine and chacruna leaves, in order for people to reconnect with spirit.

In this book, you'll read 16 first-hand accounts of profound psycho-spiritual journeys. You'll discover how this hallucinogenic tea allowed these people to access and process the hidden memories in their subconscious minds that were blocking their happiness in life.

You'll also learn how these inner journeys may have been the most difficult experiences in their lives - yet also the most liberating.

What makes the ayahuasca experience even more mysterious is the claim that there's a female spirit energy connected with the plants. Known best as, and often referred to later in this book, as 'Mother Ayahuasca'.

The ancient tradition of drinking this medicine tells us that this spirit is dedicated to the good of all humanity. and wants to help us become the best version of ourselves.

Sounds like a fairytale...

It doesn't quite work out that way though. In order to find those qualities of compassion, kindness, and love, it often requires working through the darkest aspects of your psyche. There are difficult encounters with your shadow self. Painful memories from childhood and past experiences must be processed so you can finally let them go.

Mother Ayahuasca clearly pinpoints what no longer serves you. She wakes you up from sleepwalking through life. She let's you see what you were completely blind to for so long. It's then up to you make different choices to have a different experience of life.

Ayahuasca is illegal where I live in the UK. It's also banned in the US and most other countries who have demonised the medicine as a dangerous drug. In the wrong hands - yes it could be.

But used traditionally in a ceremony with the right people, in the right setting, and with the right intentions, ayahuasca is arguably the most powerful medicine known to man.

That's why an ever-increasing number of Westerners are travelling to countries like Peru and Brazil every year to drink the medicine in the jungle. It's why hundreds of ayahuasca healing retreats are now operating in European countries like Portugal, the Netherlands and Spain, transforming lives every day.

At the same time, an ayahuasca industry that's largely unregulated has developed and experiences can vary. That's why this book also includes a chapter at the end to help people choose a safe retreat that's right for them.

The purpose of this book is not to debate the legality of ayahuasca or force my opinion on it down your throat. I certainly won't be claiming it's right for you, or a cure-all, because it's absolutely not.

I've written this book for other people who have recently come across ayahuasca for the first time. It's for men and women who are considering drinking this plant medicine to try and solve their long-standing problems in life, but want to learn more about it first.

When ayahuasca first crossed my path I felt a strong pull towards it. I spent 16 hours per day reading every article I could find about it online, watching countless YouTube videos, and checking out every book I could get my hands on.

What I was digging deepest for were real life stories. People who were going through what I was going through. True tales of people who had overcome their worst issues drinking ayahuasca - and could give me hope for achieving the same.

Hours and hours of trawling the internet would deliver the odd individual story that I could relate to, but I still had plenty of questions.

I wanted more first hand accounts because saying yes to this medicine was a big decision. I wanted more 'before and after' stories that would give me the confidence to venture into the unknown since this medicine labelled an illegal, dangerous drug in my country.

That's the purpose of writing this book: to provide you with a collection of real life stories all contained within these pages. Details of the struggles people just like you are facing, and how ayahuasca helped them find answers, find healing, and ultimately find themselves.

That's why I chose to title this book *The Healing Power of Ayahuasca: 16 Incredible Life Transformations That Will Inspire Your Self-Discovery*. And the themes of healing and self-discovery run throughout all of them.

Healing sexual abuse trauma, depression, PTSD, addictions, eating disorders, overwhelming fear, painful grief, chronic health issues, and more are covered in these inspiring true stories.

Surprising cases of self-discovery where people realise they're not who think they are; that they've created a character with their own special set of behaviours in order to feel safe, loved, and wanted.

They discover they've unconsciously built themselves up with so much armour as a result of childhood trauma and painful experiences later in life.

Ayahuasca pulls off that armour, piece by piece. The medicine takes you back to important places and situations you've forgotten about before your behaviours were born. It holds up a mirror of reality so that you can see the real you for the first time.

I spent many months in 2018 tracking down people of all ages and nationalities who had drunk ayahuasca. They were all struggling with mental, physical and emotional baggage, and came to the medicine desperate for healing. They all wanted to fill that emptiness and discover a more fulfilled life where they could finally feel a real connection and love.

I teamed up with them to share their stories with you. If you, and only you, take inspiration from any of the following incredible journeys of healing and recovery, then this book has done its job.

Their transformations show that there is hope. Hope beyond pharmaceuticals that only deal with symptoms and never treat the root cause. Hope beyond mainstream medicine where our Western society gets sicker.

Hope for a healthier, happier future…where you can be the real you.

CHAPTER 1

~

I was looking for my brother - but found myself

Ciaran Martin was speeding along the motorway heading towards Galway.

In the car he was on the right road. In his life he was completely lost.

Oncoming traffic shot past more quickly as he pressed down on the accelerator. His body was tense, his mind was frantic, and he was struggling to push out the dark thoughts.

Suddenly they were interrupted as Ciaran's ex-girlfriend called his mobile phone. She wanted to check up on him because it was only a week since Deco had died.

Deco was Ciaran's younger brother, aged only 26. More than a decade of drug addiction and living a chaotic lifestyle cut the young man's life short suddenly on October 5th, 2016.

Drug abuse was rife where the lads lived in Ireland. The pair were both taking hard drugs from the age of 15…and barely a day passed when they weren't snorting cocaine, taking ecstasy or whatever they could get their hands on.

It was their only escape - but Ciaran had no idea what they were trying to escape from.

Deco had some spiritual experiences before he died and even predicted his own death to his big brother. In the midst of the all grief, confusion and pain in the aftermath of it really happening, Ciaran's life spiralled out of control and he was on the brink of being buried alongside his brother.

But the unexpected phone call from his ex-girlfriend was a temporary distraction. They chatted for a while until Ciaran reached his sister's house in Galway. That was his safe place for the night - away from the chaos of his home town…but still not away from the chaos in his own mind.

Waking up the following morning, Ciaran quickly looked for some form of mental stimulation, something else to focus on before the negativity tornado could come crashing in again.

"I logged onto Facebook - and the first thing I saw was a post about ayahuasca retreats with Inner Mastery," said Ciaran. "It was like an omen. The minute I saw it I just knew. I instantly knew I had to go.

"I didn't know what to expect. I had no idea the medicine was taken in a ceremony, or how it would affect me. But the pull was so strong towards it that I couldn't help but become entangled in it."

Flights were booked. Intentions were set. Within a fortnight Ciaran was 800 miles away in Eindhoven, the Netherlands, in a small darkened room with 12 strangers.

The young Irishman was nervous and retreated to a table in a corner of the room. Ciaran sat quietly…he didn't want to get involved in any conversation with the others. He was too nervous and felt like he was barely holding things together.

As he cowered with his head down, a big Colombian man in the group slowly walked towards him. He sat down next to Ciaran, and said: "My friend, are you addicted to cocaine?"

This stranger invited Ciaran to open up. He would not judge him - he was from the cocaine capital of the world after all.

They sat down with the rest of the group as each of them began to tell their story. He'd been avoiding chatting to the others, but Ciaran quickly realised this was exactly what he needed.

Another Colombian man spoke with pain in his voice about his brother being kidnapped by a gang and then murdered. His brother was tortured and his final hours were agony. His arms and legs were hacked off and then thrown back at his torso as he died in the most horrifying fashion.

A young woman in the group then spoke quietly, telling the group she had been sold to a circus a few years earlier. She had been raped repeatedly and had given birth to children afterwards.

Suddenly Ciaran was given the antidote to the misery he'd been wallowing in for weeks: perspective.

He said: "I'd travelled to Eindhoven thinking about how terrible my life was, how painful it was, and how it couldn't get any worse. When I heard these heartbreaking stories that all shifted. I asked myself, 'do I even have the right to be in the room with these people'?

"Hearing what they had gone through brought me back down to earth and I realised that my life isn't really that bad."

As the group prepared for their first cup of ayahuasca in the ceremony that night, their facilitator named Bruno told them to "surrender to the mystery".

As the medicine flowed through his body, Ciaran felt a strong rush of anxiety come over him. He didn't want to surrender to anything. He wanted to run…get on a plane home…cower away…hide and go to sleep.

He could only wrap himself up tightly in his blanket on the floor. As he curled up, he squeezed his eyelids tightly shut. He didn't want to open his eyes and just wanted the increasingly uncomfortable feelings to go away.

Ciaran's focus was swiftly taken off the uneasy feelings in his body when visions of his brother appeared. Deco kept dipping in and out of his consciousness before Ciaran was thrust into a space filled with colour and energy. He struggled to make sense of it all.

"Did I contact Deco's spirit?" he said. "Maybe, I'm not sure. What I have come to realise now is that ayahuasca seems to stay with you and keeps constantly affecting you. Once you get thrown into that other realm, ayahuasca stays with you beyond that.

"Before taking the medicine I was too scared to open up about my problems. Men don't really talk about their problems where I'm from. Ayahuasca completely broke down my ego and my barriers to my issues so that I could deal with them properly. Before that my only outlet was to become sad, lose my temper, and take drugs as I struggled to cope with what was going on inside.

"Going to bed afterwards I felt like I had been ripped open and everyone was now seeing everything about me. It was clear that I had always tried to hide my feelings and put on a macho front. Ayahuasca completely shattered my perceptions of being a man."

****

In the space of several hours Ciaran had experienced a monumental shift. His world definitely wouldn't be the same. It was 11pm but by the following morning Ciaran would experience the biggest breakthrough in his life.

Ciaran woke up feeling drained. He felt exposed for the first time - like he couldn't hide from anything anymore.

He joined the group as they all sat down to take bufo. Ciaran looked around to see who would step forward first because he certainly wasn't going to. He was feeling scared after his bumpy ride with ayahuasca just a few hours earlier, and wanted someone else to be the crash test dummy for the toad poison journey.

The first guy smoked the pipe and seemed to be transported to a place of joy as he lay back smiling. This gave Ciaran the confidence to step up next. He knelt in front of Bruno and asked, "what am I going to feel?" Bruno replied: "It will feel like death and rebirth".

The facilitator saw the instant panic on Ciaran's face and assured him: "You will come back, you will be okay." Ciaran felt his calming energy and leaned into the pipe, quickly inhaling the bufo.

Ciaran saw Bruno moving backwards from him. Then the whole room started pushing backwards. Within seconds he was pulled out of his body and thrust into an empty, cold, hostile space.

He said: "It was just this empty void and there was a ying yang object spinning around really fast. It kept getting smaller and smaller, tighter and brighter, and to the point where it looked like a really small, dense, powerful star.

"I felt like I was inside that tiny star - but was all around it at the same time. I was in a dark, empty space - but simultaneously could feel and see everything."

'Everything' also meant everything Ciaran had buried from his childhood. The painful memories that he'd run so far away from and completely forgotten about were now in front of his eyes.

The physical abuse and torment he'd suffered as a boy aged only four or five had returned…and he was reliving a child's pain with the mind of an adult. The violence didn't happen directly in his home. But Ciaran was given the insight that these horrible early experiences were directly affecting his behaviour in everyday life.

He could feel his body being battered, an overwhelming wave of fear, crushing sadness and longing for love instead of hate. He fought the feelings. He frantically looked for an escape. He couldn't handle it any longer.

He shouted out: "Okay, I give in. I surrender."

In that moment the tiny ying and yang star which had shrunk to a tiny speck of light in a dark void began to change. It turned into a bright ball and Ciaran was overcome with feelings of joy and hope.

"Life itself was letting me in," he said. "Before that I'd really felt like I had died. Then the white ball started vibrating and exponentially expanding with the brightest light. Everything that ever existed was inside that white ball. Everything in the entire universe was within it and it completely engulfed me."

Ciaran felt himself re-enter his body and he was suddenly back in the room with the others. Confused and in a panic, he said: "I don't want to die." Once again, Bruno calmed him down, saying: "It's okay, it's a process."

He flew back into the experience…only this time it wasn't scary. Ciaran found himself in a lighter, happier space. He could still feel the ground below him and could still smell the ceremony room.

It represented a move away from the old, chaotic, heavy life to a new place where he feels grounded and optimistic. Before turning to the medicine Ciaran was unemployed, addicted to cocaine, in poor health, and had no hope for the future.

That first groundbreaking retreat in Eindhoven in April 2017 involved three ayahuasca ceremonies and one bufo session. It blew apart the fake persona he had created to try and protect himself from further hurt. Another three ceremonies followed at a retreat in Marbella the next month, which enabled him to let go of more past hurt and become more familiar with his real self.

Ciaran is now working as a chef, lives in a new town, and is bringing out his creative side through writing and martial arts. The 28-year-old is currently writing a book to share his story and to help other guys who are struggling with grief, depression and emotional problems.

Ciaran was made to face and process the deep, hurtful experiences that he thought he'd buried, but that were haunting him. He'd crafted a strong, aggressive, loud, macho character as a way of poorly patching up a deep wound…and drowning out his crying inner child.

The bandage had come off and the child was never going to stop crying until he got attention.

Ciaran said: "Men often always feel the need to be strong and can't show their emotions. I saw it all around me where I lived and sadly drugs and drink is the only escape for some people. I've lost my brother and friends who were all struggling.

"I'd been portraying this tough outward persona when really I was hiding this deep insecurity that was caused by other people who had abused me. I turned to ayahuasca to find my brother - but I found myself."

CHAPTER 2

⌒

War is over

Fred Hoogervorst cowered on the floor close to his mother and grabbed her tightly.

His body was shaking. They huddled together in the centre of the living room alongside Fred's three older brothers. All were scared yet confused at the same time. The noises getting louder. The walls and furniture vibrating. Fred's father pinned mattresses up against the door, hoping these would keep the family safe.

Little Fred shut his eyes and put his hands over his ears as another blast sounded outside. Bomb after bomb. To Fred it seemed like each one was coming closer to their home.

Why was this happening in Rotterdam? Were these German fighter planes not supposed to be bombing England instead? Was it safe to even stay indoors? Just some of questions Fred's panicked parents were frantically asking each other as the chaos erupted outside.

Swarms of people were darting around in the street below their third-floor home. Many of them leaving everything behind and running for the open fields. The Hoogervorsts were intent on sticking together and staying inside. Until the smoke came…

Incendiary bombs landed just a few hundred yards from their building. A large fire quickly took hold and dark, thick smoke was filling the air. It was time to leave in case the blaze spread and the family were trapped inside.

It was May 14th, 1940. Four days earlier Germany had declared war on the Netherlands. The Dutch army had initially held firm, but when the Germans began bombing Rotterdam early in the afternoon of May 14th everything changed.

Buildings blasted to pieces. Entire families wiped out. Fire spreading through the city and thousands made homeless every hour. The Dutch high command was forced to surrender that same night.

Fred was just nine years old…scared and seeking nothing but safety.

Fred's father hurriedly pulled the mattresses away from the living room door and guided the family downstairs. They joined the chaotic scenes outside but his father stayed calm - and had a plan. He pointed the way and the six of them ran through the streets together.

"We were scared but my father knew what he was doing and had it under control," said Fred. Almost 80 years on and his memories of that night were still so clear.

"He led us to a safe place. We were taken to a big house that belonged to my father's employer. The employer had built a bomb shelter in his garden and, as my father was very close with his family, we stayed with them in the shelter for a couple of days."

Almost a thousand people were killed, eighty thousand left homeless. Fred, his parents and brothers all survived. Their home was also untouched and they all returned safely after a few days.

The Hoogervorsts were relieved to be alive but the German occupation of Rotterdam afterwards ripped the family apart. Fred's eldest brother, Frans, was captured by the Nazis and sent to work in German factories.

In 1944 it looked like Fred's other brothers, Kees, 17, and Tom, 16, would also become slaves to the German war effort. But Fred's father, who had joined the Resistance, helped them escape to secret underground locations.

Rotterdam was decaying under German control and residents struggled to survive with wartime rations. Winter in 1944/45 hit hard and 20,000 people in Rotterdam and other cities in the Western part of the country starved to death.

The war would not end for another nine months. Fred and his family had to take drastic action just to survive another day.

He said: "We were eating flower bulbs, sugar beets, whatever we could lay our hands on. I, myself, was catching seagulls. I caught 12 of them on the roof and these were put in the soup. A pot of water was always boiling on the stove, and whatever we got our hands on we put in the soup.

"My father always told me, 'first comes your family - and then the other part of the community'. Look after yourself. Look after yourself. Look after yourself. That is what he drummed into my head.

"I later discovered that this had become a strong part of myself that I needed to give up.

"My mother and father were looking after their boys, but there was a lot of fear. I felt the tension."

On May 5th, 1945, the Canadian army liberated the city. The Dutch people cheered as the Canadians marched through his town. Fred was elated. He was free.

His feelings of fear and memories from the nights Rotterdam was bombed? They were not free. The constant anxiety and uncertainty under German occupation? Those memories were buried in his subconscious mind and the emotions got stuck in his body. The survival instinct that his father had taught him? That had become a part of Fred.

****

After serving in the army for two years, Fred earned a job as financial controller with a Dutch multinational firm in the pharmaceutical industry.

Aged 26, he married Truus. They had two girls and a son, and were together for 52 years until Truus died. The top finance job led Fred and his family around the world.

They lived for 10 years in West Africa, then Iran, and eventually returned to Rotterdam. The finance chief role developed negative feelings and behaviours in Fred.

Being vigilant for fraud, keeping a constant check on spending, and being sent in as a company troubleshooter changed him as a person. He gradually became more cynical and had a growing distrust of other people along the way.

These negative energies were piled upon those already stuck in his body from his youth during the war. He often felt tense, he became reactive, and his mind was in complete control.

Exercise and always staying active in retirement kept his body fit, and also provided a break from his busy thoughts. Sailing on fresh water and the sea, jogging, boxing…all of it was a healthy distraction from what was really going on inside.

Then, aged 69, visits to a medium with his wife began to create shifts in Fred's life.

"You've always lived in your head," she told him. "Start painting and writing. Expand your creativity and live more from the heart."

Fred said: "Through painting and writing poems I became much more creative. Through this practice I discovered my Inner Self, my centre from which this creativity springs off.

"Then I also started discovering what you really feel - not from your ego - but from your soul. I started trying to live from my heart, not my head, trusting inner feelings and intuition."

Fred continued along the spiritual path after his wife died in 2009. Three years later, he met Annette, another widow who was also a spiritual seeker. Together a new journey was about to begin.

In 2013, Fred's life was plunged into crisis as he was diagnosed with myositis, a muscle disease. Almost overnight he couldn't climb the stairs anymore. His legs, arms and neck muscles all affected.

As the condition worsened, Fred couldn't swallow his food. A probe was placed in his stomach and he was admitted to hospital for three weeks.

Medics made the diagnosis and gave him medication for the symptoms. Yet Fred soon discovered the root cause of this sudden illness. The subtle shifts he was making spiritually were drawing his attention to unfinished business - unresolved trauma he'd been hanging onto for far too long.

All linked to fear, tension and survival conditions in his youth during the war, together with some bad experiences as an adult. These memories had long been buried in his subconscious mind and the feelings continually stifled throughout his life.

It was time to dig them up and deal with them.

Fred and Annette bumped into Gerard and Ellie at an expo event in Western Holland in early 2015. It wasn't long before the conversation turned to ayahuasca and Fred became instantly curious.

How long had they been working with this medicine? How was it helping people? More importantly, could he and Annette join one of their ceremonies to drink it?

****

A few months later Fred and Annette were sitting in a room with a dozen strangers along with Gerard, Ellie and fellow ayahuasca facilitator Nicolette. All together at the Mens en Aandacht retreat in Southern Holland and preparing for journeys within themselves.

He was the oldest person to ever drink ayahuasca at the retreat, at the age of 84. Annette was not far behind, aged 76.

As Fred lay on the mattress, he eased into the journey very relaxed. As the first hour passed, the mood of the room gradually changed. People nearby him were crying, some were vomiting, and one was beating his mattress. Fred remained still, feeling at peace.

The medicine took Fred back to his childhood. Not the war years, but the other good times he spent with his family. No visions or dramatic scenes, just enjoying being a boy.

Fred's adult mind guiding his inner child through the experience, talking to himself throughout, explaining the thoughts and emotions that were coming up and allowing them to be processed.

Love and a deep respect was the major theme of this journey: love for his parents and older brothers. A strong respect for his parents, properly appreciating how they always protected their sons. How they minimised the mental war damage on their boys while struggling with fear for their own lives.

Fred was deep in his own sea of emotions. The medicine rewinding through decades of his life, while gently allowing his body to release stuck energies. Tears that rolled down his cheeks occasionally brought his awareness back into his body. Thoughts of his late wife made him smile and heightened the loving feelings.

Five months later, Fred and Annette were back at Mens en Aandacht. Six more days, three more ayahuasca journeys, and yearning for a closer look at their past, their relationships and their place in life.

Each night after his ceremony was over Fred reached for his pen and his diary. Here's what he wrote…

Fourth experience on 19th October, 2015

A kind of anthropological trip.

The enormous space and silence when sailing on the sea, where I also felt enormous energy. It felt as if I was an isle of feelings.

It became clear to me that I must get an apartment. A very quiet place where I can paint, write poems and study my inner self. My head was full of life experiences that were gained and understood, but I must let my body in its own way get rid of energetic blockages.

This felt good to me for curing my myositis.

Fifth experience on 20th October, 2015

Felt my mother close to me. It felt as if I was four years old again and I felt very safe with her.

Later on I told her that I had the feeling in a kind of family-line way; I had rounded off her bitterness and humiliation in her youth at home, in my own life.

I thanked my father for what he did for his family and told him to be proud of himself. Then I sent my greetings and love to my three brothers.

Again I experienced this being an isle of feelings. Feel I am clearly rounding off my life well.

Sixth experience on 22nd October, 2015

A great variety of emotions came along. All related to episodes in my life in Holland, as well as abroad, from my youth, being responsible for my family etc.

Survival emotions came up on many occasions, like in winter 1945, starvation in Rotterdam. As a 14 year old boy sitting alone in the loft and killing 12 seagulls. Caught these birds on a line on the roof to eat. In these war days they were part of our meal.

The irony of life as this boy was already a birdwatcher from his youngest days (and still is).

It's amazing how much you learn from the experience and life of the other participants. How colourful and tough life can be.

Comparing what I experienced to them was a pretty straightforward life irrespective of how it hurt me emotionally.

Fred and Annette continued returning to Mens en Aandacht every 4-6 months. Each cup of ayahuasca bringing a release and sense of lightness. Fred always feeling calm, always clear in his mind, always at peace...no matter what was going on around him.

The medicine filled Fred with confidence to go deeper into his own psyche, removing what had not served him in life.

A big breakthrough came on 24th September, 2016. Ceremony number 10. The most physical one yet as ayahuasca clawed out what no longer belonged with Fred.

"I saw a short image of buildings with a very depressing atmosphere," explained Fred. "The atmosphere had a certain threat hanging there. I didn't like it at all, but I thought that if this becomes frightening I must let it happen.

"This feeling and scene repeated a few times and I stayed present in my body without trying to run away.

"I started vomiting and it felt as if a box filled with cynical contents was pulled out of my body. I literally fell over as I felt it being dragged out of me. After this my body felt at complete rest inside; it was glorious. My body started shaking lightly and tears rolled over my cheeks.

"For me it was this cynical energy blockage leaving my life. It never came back. It meant to me that I had finally overcome an important mental shadow."

Ayahuasca has shown Fred he's on the right path at the later stage of his life. Bringing balance, peace and rounding off his life perfectly by letting go of what was hurting him.

"I'm living very calm at my apartment," he said. "I have no problems whatsoever. I still enjoy reading and writing. I feel even closer to nature when I'm out walking, and I feel that there are so many other dimensions I am connected with.

"My brain just doesn't have the capacity to understand it all. I trust in life. I have a feeling that the meaning of my life is good."

Aged 87 and still taking part in ceremonies in 2018, Fred could be the oldest ayahuasca drinker in Europe. His wartime trauma began in 1940 when the first bombs dropped in Rotterdam…and it finally ended when Canadian soldiers liberated the city on May 5th, 1945.

That special day had long been forgotten. However, in his second ayahuasca ceremony in May 2015 Mother Ayahuasca decided it was time for Fred to go back there.

His body lay on the mattress at the Mens en Aandacht retreat like before but Fred was elsewhere. Feeling forever young, he relived one of the best moments of his life.

Tanks rolled through the street with Canadian soldiers walking behind them. People were cheering, shouting, hugging the soldiers. An atmosphere of pure joy.

He saw himself sitting watching it all happen from the corner of the street. Aged 14, he couldn't stop smiling and had tears in his eyes. He had never felt more excited. More free.

Fred opened his eyes and smiled at his facilitator Nicolette, who was sitting beside him. "I feel liberated," he told her. Fred shared with Nicolette how he had just re-experienced that glorious day in May.

He told her: "It was like I was back there as a boy again. I felt all the same feelings as I did when the Canadians came and freed the city."

Nicolette replied: "Fred, today is May 5th! It is the anniversary of the liberation."

CHAPTER 3

~

I just want to be seen

Annette sat on the school bus feeling nervous about the destination ahead.

On this particular day she wasn't heading for the classroom. The seven-year-old girl was leaving the country instead. The bus was packed with other children from her home town of Breda in the southern part of the Netherlands.

It was 1946. Annette was going to live with another family in Belgium for a month. She didn't know the family, but was told it would be an adventure; an exciting holiday she should be looking forward to.

But this child was far from pleased. Why do I have to leave? Why am I going away for so long? Why can't I see my brothers? Annette asked herself all of those questions as she tried to make sense of the strange situation.

Annette's friends from school were also travelling to live with families they didn't know. It was a year since the Second World War had ended

- and someone thought it would be beneficial if the children were given a holiday to recuperate from the after-effects.

Annette was born in 1939, the year war broke out, and the city of Breda had been occupied by the Germans for the majority of her young life. Annette's parents thought she would enjoy living with the family in Belgium that had agreed to let her stay.

Within an hour of walking into the house, Annette knew she was going to hate it. Within a few days, she realised it was going to be anything but a holiday. The man, woman and their three boys brought the shy little Dutch girl indoors…and the introductions got off to the worst possible start.

"You call me mama," said the lady of the house. It was a firm instruction, rather than a question. All eyes were on little Annette. The father, mother, and three boys she would be sharing a home with for the next month, all put her on the spot.

Annette looked up directly at the woman, and responded: "You are not my mama."

The woman's eyelids widened in disbelief - and then immediately narrowed in anger. Annette was not being who she wanted her to be, or doing what she expected her to do. From that moment on, Annette's stay in Belgium was made as uncomfortable as possible. The woman terrorised her.

Wakened early each day, Annette was ordered outside into the chicken house and forced to do heavy lifting work. Indoors, the youngster was given chore after chore, day after day. Some days Annette was so exhausted that she had to give up. That's when the serious punishment occurred.

"Kneel down! Kneel down!" screamed the lady of the house. Annette slowly crouched down to the floor where the wooden shoes were placed directly in front of her. She felt the hard edges of the shoes dig into her knees and, as they grazed her skin, Annette started crying. The pressure on her knees was so painful, but the lady of the house had no sympathy. To her this punishment was deserved. To Annette it was horrifying.

Later, the woman who was supposed to be caring for Annette forced her to write a letter confessing that she'd stolen her money. It was lies, but Annette was ordered to write as the woman stood watching over her. It wasn't an easy thing to do for a seven-year-old. When Annette looked up and asked how to spell a difficult word she was berated and mocked.

Continuing her campaign of bullying a child, the woman even got the village police officer to put Annette in jail for a few hours. A frightening lesson for the young girl as another punishment for 'stealing' money.

Annette said: "This monstrous woman informed my parents of this act and I was sent home after one month. I later discovered that the very same thing happened to other children as well.

"Because of this incident my parents were angry, sad and felt ashamed. Whenever I said I was innocent they did not believe me. I also never had a chance to tell them about my punishments and this woman's behaviour.

"When I was aged 13 I heard for the very first time that my parents already knew shortly after my return from Belgium that I had not stolen money. From that very same day I lost what was left of my confidence in them."

Lacking trust and confidence in her parents, Annette began to rebel. As a teenager she resisted what they wanted her to do. She became stubborn, aggressive, and refused to listen to her parents. As the years passed, Annette became more difficult to handle and left the family home aged 18.

Despite her childhood troubles and poor relationship with her parents, Annette was determined that she was going to be successful. She'd prove to them all that she didn't need them to get by in life.

She immediately started working and studying as a school teacher in Delft, a city 70km away from Breda. Annette later became head of the school, and appeared to be living a stable, happy life on the outside.

Yet there was a huge hole in Annette's world. An emptiness in her heart. She carried with her an inner child that felt invisible. Never seen, heard, believed or understood.

****

Anna's earliest years were spent in an atmosphere of fear and intimidation when German soldiers ruled their town. Enduring one month of misery at the hands of a cruel stranger she never wanted to live with in the first place. Then returning home and feeling unloved, insignificant, and unworthy for 'bringing shame' on her family.

That turbulent, confusing, messy period occurred as Annette was still developing emotionally as a child. The years she sought the most love, affection, and protection, she was often met with blame, guilt and fear instead.

As an adult there were often moments of shyness and holding back from properly expressing herself. Annette simply never felt good enough. Immersing herself in sports including running, skiing, horse riding and golf helped gradually build up her confidence. Doing ballet and walking in nature made her more comfortable too.

Annette worked for 30 years as head of the school, and after 16 years her husband passed away. They had no children. Aged 46, Annette started studying again - as a psychological social therapist in Utrecht. She wanted to help others, and to better understand herself.

There she'd become friends with Femke - and first heard about ayahuasca. Femke was familiar with Ayahuasca. She'd trained with shamans in the Amazon and was a member of the Santo Daime church. Annette was always fascinated listening to Femke's stories about the intriguing jungle medicine, but she quickly ruled out drinking it due to suffering heart problems at the time.

By 2015, Annette's long-awaited opportunity came. She finally drank Ayahuasca for the first time - aged 76. Annette and 85-year-old partner Fred arrived at the Mens en Aandacht retreat in Holland ready for the unknown.

Annette's intention: to find out her place in this world and the meaning of her life. Before drinking her cup of ayahuasca, Annette closed her eyes and asked in her mind: "who am I and what is my mission on earth?"

The effects of the ayahuasca came on fairly quickly. Annette lay back on her mattress, keeping her eyes closed. Suddenly she was in China. There were crowds of people around her. Men and women crying, extremely angry, and some looked scared. Annette didn't understand why these people were all in distress, but it made her feel sullen.

The journey moved on and Annette found herself lying in a dark pit. With no doors or any apparent way to escape, she began to panic. Was anyone coming to save her? Would she starve to death in there?

Annette was dazed and confused. "Why am I in this dark pit?", she asked. The message came that she was a high priestess in Egypt in this particular past life. She'd ruthlessly judged over people's life and death. A terrible mistake - and she was being made to pay by being thrown in the pit for punishment.

There was no way out on her own, so Annette asked for help. A small sunbeam appeared from above. It expanded and got brighter, showing her the way upwards. Annette followed the light out of the darkness and, on finally escaping, was abruptly wakened up from her visions with the immediate need to vomit.

She leaned over the basin at the side of her mattress and started to purge. With the dark liquid leaving her body, it felt like every one of Annette's cells were being cleaned out. The facilitators watched over her, cared for her, and helped Annette comprehend her disturbing past-life episode.

Despite finding herself temporarily trapped and feeling scared and anxious in that initial journey, those feelings of fear were replaced once the effects of ayahuasca had worn off. Instead, Annette became curious about what other past lives she might discover. Intrigued about what other dark aspects to these characters may still be lingering with her.

Ceremony two came, then three. Annette delved deeper into her own psyche, returning to the same Dutch retreat again, and again with Fred. Seventeen ceremonies in around two years. In four of them, she was transported back to China where there was unfinished business.

Annette said: "I felt and saw plenty of pain, sorrow and fear. I felt this very much in myself. The lesson was clear: look and see but don't feel. I learned not to take other people's sorrow on my neck but to only observe it instead."

The burden of taking on other's people's pain and problems in life had clearly weighed down on Annette. Ayahuasca helped lift that load from her back, and brought her a sense of belonging she had craved since childhood. The need to be seen, heard and acknowledged was finally fulfilled.

"I got the message that I was 'seen' by the Masters," she said. "Years ago I received priceless lessons from the astral world through my friend Elia, a medium. Elia always spoke on behalf of 'the Masters of Light and Healing'.

"I feel that I am supported by them when helping people in my work as a psychotherapist."

Now aged 79, Annette is still a practicing psychotherapist in Holland. She supports people with lingering mental problems, those who suffered traumatic experiences in their youth, and people struggling with their emotions in relationships.

She said: "Ayahuasca has improved my intuitive insight into people's problems. I know the solution to their problems deep inside myself, a matter of knowing for certain. The ayahuasca experiences have also strengthened my love and compassion for people.

"I see many much younger people drinking Ayahuasca. That is encouraging as they find solace in getting rid of their anger, sorrow, misery and other frustrations. I see hope and comfort for the future.

"Before ayahuasca I was always seeking myself and never felt good enough. I've been led to meet the right people in my life and healed myself. I have forgiven that Belgian lady and feel sorry and compassion for her. And above all, I have forgiven my parents."

CHAPTER 4

⌒

It's all about kindness

"Do not make me have to teach you this lesson again!"

Stephen heard the strongly-worded message loud and clear. It felt like his mother was telling him off as a child for arguing with his brothers or being cheeky at home.

Only this time he was around 700 miles from his home in Scotland. He wasn't a child, he was aged 34. And it wasn't his mother giving him a warning…it was Mother Ayahuasca.

Stephen sat up sharply from the mattress he was lying on. The English couple were still lying on the floor to his right, while the couple from Sweden were still deep into their ayahuasca journeys.

Stephen waved over Delilah, one of the guides at the retreat, and hugged her. "I know what I need to do now," he told Delilah. She smiled warmly, and asked him: "Do you want another cup of ayahuasca?"

"Don't need it," Stephen quickly replied. "I've got everything I came here for."

This was Stephen's fourth ayahuasca experience. It was the most powerful and it felt like he'd just filled up his fuel tank to hit the road of life again.

Just three years earlier, the tank was empty after Stephen's brother John had died unexpectedly. It all happened so fast in the summer of 2014. Stephen fixed the funeral arrangements, he fixed his thoughts on his career. What he wasn't able to fix was the relationship with John before he died.

They'd rowed over his brother's drug-taking. How it had upset their parents. Resentment and anger had been building for many years...and now he was saddled with guilt, grief, shame and sadness instead.

Stephen's way of extinguishing them? Becoming more career driven. Partying more at weekends. Emotionally cutting himself off from those that he loved. Delving more into self-destructive habits.

His emotions were given the cold shoulder, but he stumbled across an 18 minute ayahuasca video online that really turned up the heat. Stephen was hooked on Graham Hancock's initially banned - and now infamous - 'war on consciousness' Ted Talk video on YouTube.

"It was like someone had lit a fire underneath me," said Stephen. "I suppose it was what's widely known as 'the calling' when ayahuasca touches your life.

"I went from watching a 20 minute video to reading everything I could find about the medicine, watching every video available, and trying to discover everything I could about it. It became like an obsession."

Ayahuasca occupied his thoughts constantly, but Stephen felt alone with it. None of his friends or family had even heard about it, never mind understood it.

Still, he made contact with Ayahuasca International and, on September 17, 2015, Stephen arrived at the retreat in Madrid. He was like a man split in two. Part of him wanted to run back to the airport and the other half wanted to embrace the mysterious journey and be taken in a new direction.

Stephen walked through the gates of the villa into a garden area. Around 10 people were already standing there talking in the sunshine around an empty swimming pool.

While Stephen still felt a little tense, the vibe in the garden area was surprisingly relaxed. A guy called Steve from Leeds in England shook his hand, introduced himself, and they chatted for an hour before everyone took their place in the ceremonial room.

It was a large square space with a fireplace at the far end, and the shaman named Cesar sitting directly in front of it.

Three guides walked round the room asking people why they were there and to focus on their intentions.

Stephen stepped forward first to take the medicine and lay back as one of the guides started playing bongo drums. Another facilitator began telling a story about how man had strayed and had broken his connection with spirit. This was leading to all our problems and illnesses, the guide told the room.

Stephen tuned in. It took his mind off trying to predict what effects ayahuasca would have on him. He closed his eyes and heard gentle piano music playing. Then came the the bright psychedelic colours, which slowly started to swamp his vision.

A jolt hit his body and Stephen felt being forced off the floor into a sitting position. A wave of emotion was coming - and he was being made to sit upright to face it. All connected to the relationship with his brother.

There was guilt over the rows they had. Sadness about how John's life was cut short by drugs. Shame about how he'd judged him. The pain of not being able to make peace with him before he died. Unable to tell him again that he loved him.

They were very close as young boys. He loved the way his big brother could make everyone laugh. He admired his footballing skills, his taste in music, his personality, his kindness.

All of that had been forgotten because John had fallen into a chaotic drugs lifestyle, like so many others in the West of Scotland. They never got to say goodbye. Stephen never got to grieve properly either as he was too busy organising the funeral and trying to stay strong for his parents.

The tears started flowing as Stephen sat with his chin resting on his arm. It felt like the medicine had caused the river of emotions within Stephen to burst its banks and there was no way it could be stopped.

He wept uncontrollably for an hour - in a room filled with 18-20 strangers. It didn't matter, Stephen knew it was okay to feel grief. No need to hang onto it any longer…and he soon discovered he didn't have a choice anyway.

"I felt someone walk up behind me and physically take something off my back," he explained. "Like someone had put their hand on my shoulder and lifted this emotional weight from my body.

"I then had the understanding that my brother simply had his problems and I have mine, and could see things from a completely different perspective."

Stephen lay back, feeling lighter and refreshed, as the grief left and only positive memories remained. Then the theme of the journey switched to his own lifestyle. The constant partying and feeding his ego, and how he wasn't looking after his body and mind properly.

He said: "I was shown visions of myself meditating and was getting the message that I need to look after myself. That I don't have to prove myself and be the last man standing at the party.

"There were visions of me in this huge orb, meditating and being at peace. Like I was being told to dedicate myself to meditation."

The shaman called upon the group to come forward for another cup of ayahuasca. Stephen felt drained, dizzy, tired. He was first to step forward and experience ayahuasca this evening, but this time he just lay there resting.

Within seconds he had the vision of a green female figure with muscular legs. She had the head of an owl and her body was covered in leaves, branches, pieces of forestry. She was there to acknowledge him for finally listening to his body and taking care of it.

The following night Stephen picked up his mat and fled the ceremony room. The visions were too dark and sinister. Spiders, insects, animals crept into his mind while a sense of panic rushed in.

He wanted to escape this anxiety filled place. He'd purged violently just 30 minutes into the ceremony and it had left him feeling weak.

"I'm not enjoying this," he'd said to one of the guides. "Maybe you're not supposed to," came the blunt response.

Stephen lay outside in the cold air with his hands wrapped around his stomach and his eyes tightly shut. The menacing movie kept playing in his mind, only interrupted by regular bouts of purging.

The vomit came hard and fast. Stephen knew he needed to get it out. He also wanted it to stop and his mind frantically searched for a way out.

This time there wasn't an exit. No one could take this away. He'd tried to control all his experiences in life and this was a test to change that broken approach.

He was failing miserably. Stephen wailed and moaned about wanting the experience to stop before one of the guides rushed towards him.

The guide grabbed Stephen's shoulder and said: "Don't rob yourself of the power to heal. Get on with it!"

It was like his father had given him a stern talking to. It was exactly what he needed. As Stephen relaxed his tense body and lay back surrendering to the battle, suddenly there was no battle at all.

Instead, he'd time travelled almost 30 years. Shot back into his childhood, Stephen watched as he was back sitting on his mum's knee. Aged around six, in the living room of the house he grew up in. Every detail of the room that had been long forgotten, filed away in his subconscious library, was now clear to see.

The flower patterned curtains, the room's blue decor, family photos of him and his brothers on the wall. There he was in the centre of the room and also the centre of attention surrounded by women: his mum, his aunts, and his gran.

All were showering him with love and attention. They poured positive reinforcement into his young developing mind. He saw them showing how much they cared and adored him.

Stephen got the message. This was when his ego was born. This was when he became the little emperor and an expectation to be adored and receive attention throughout his life began. He'd never compromised on it. Always demanded it in his relationships with women. This was what he needed to work on.

****

The 'after-glow' of the medicine followed Stephen back home to Scotland. For the first time he knew what it was like to be present in his life. He was slowly adapting to a new level of consciousness.

The glow dimmed as time went on and internal shifts also led to shifts in his outer world. Within six months, he was commuting to a new job at the other end of the country and his struggling marriage had broken down.

Tensions remained high between Stephen and his wife following their separation. Problems were popping up in his job. Stephen constantly worried how the family break-up was affecting his toddler son. The emotional weight that had been lifted from his back was replaced with another heavy load.

A year later, his back was breaking. He was breaking. Stephen knew it was time for another meeting with Mother Ayahuasca.

It was October 27th, 2017. This time Stephen had landed at a retreat in the countryside in the Netherlands. His journey would take place in a cottage surrounded by fields with horses and a wooded area in the distance where he would go for walks to integrate his experience.

There were two main facilitators, one assistant, and only five people had booked up for this retreat: a couple from England, another couple from Sweden, and Stephen. A more intimate style of retreat which made Stephen feel more relaxed.

The ceremony was also completely different from his last experience in Spain. First he shared his intention with the small group. He spoke of healing the emotional trauma from the break-up of his marriage, letting go of self-destructive patterns in relationships, and trying to become a better person to avoid future hurt.

A deck of tarot-style cards was then spread on the floor. Stephen picked out the "thunderbolt" card which featured a picture of two people jumping from a burning building. The card read: "After the fire the earth is replenished, after the storm the air is clear".

This was to be the theme of his ayahuasca journey.

Sat together in a circle, a bowl of black liquid was then passed round the small group. Each of them took a teaspoonful of the liquid into the palm of their hands and then snorted it in preparation for their ayahuasca journey.

It was mapacho - the sacred tobacco medicine from the Amazon. Stephen felt a stinging, burning sensation as soon as the liquid shot up his nose. His eyes watered and he spluttered.

The group were told that holotropic breathing was next. A form of breathing quickly that would bring emotions to the surface and release past hurt, the guides explained.

Stephen was sceptical. He didn't think he'd be able to get into it. His mind was creating resistance before the background music had even began.

But this wasn't about his mind, it was all about his breath. As he focused on his breathing, deeper and faster, he sharply felt a strong sense of loss and separation.

In full flow, his thoughts suddenly switched from his breathing to a vivid memory of his first day at primary school: being separated from his mum, crying for her, and losing that emotional connection as he was being ushered into class.

Stephen cried uncontrollably. Delilah, one of the guides, held his hand. Somehow she knew what he was re-experiencing. "Mummy is here," she said as she stroked his hand gently.

Stephen felt waves of energy surge through his body as he released the tears. It felt incredible. Less than an hour later and he was ready for his third ayahuasca journey.

With his eyes shut and attempting to meditate as the brew washed through his system, it wasn't long before the experience began. Stephen was shot into the same dark space as his previous journey, only this time he was in a different mindset. He was calm. He was an observer, not there to judge or control.

He stepped into this spirit world where a giant entity stood in control of this realm. He was a huge powerful figure, draped in purple and red, and with a star on his forehead. His every movement dictated what happened in this realm.

This god-like entity was aware of Stephen's presence, but was passive. Looking up, Stephen saw a glass ceiling with various shapes and colours behind it. It looked like lots of feet were moving around and it was a lesson that there are other realities far beyond what we live and breathe each day.

Brought back to earth, Stephen was moving through a forest of trees. He saw the vision of a woman crying at a tree - and then he became part of the tree. It didn't feel right; the land below felt damaged. The environmental damage humans are causing to planet earth every day? Stephen wasn't too sure as the medicine wore off.

The following day that group stretched their tired bodies with some yoga and spoke about their experiences at breakfast and later as they strolled through the woods. Back at the cottage in the evening, ceremony number two followed the same format of mapacho and holotropic breathing before drinking ayahuasca.

There were no tears during the breathwork this time, but going into the ceremony, Stephen had been dwelling on the hurt caused by his marriage break-up and in past relationships.

He'd spent so much time beating himself up about his marriage split and the effect on his son. He drank the brew and asked Mother Ayahuasca: "Show me joy, be gentle."

His stomach warmed as Stephen was absorbed into a deep, never ending rainbow of colours. Then it was like the lights had been switched off. Complete darkness. Another black void, yet he knew he'd been there before.

Stephen was all alone. No one there to speak to, or confide in, laugh with. He felt tension take over his body as the sense of utter loneliness struck him in the heart.

Then it was clear. He'd often been alone as he'd tried to figure out life's problems. He'd unknowingly isolated himself in a macho attempt to take care of everything that had gone wrong in his world. His ego had always told him he had the brain power to make everything right, be his own hero. Never needing support.

That supposedly strong approach to life had left him weak. It had taken him to this black, lifeless, island of nothingness. He felt stranded and hopeless.

The pressure built in his body, an unstoppable purge was coming. Stephen's mind switched back to the card he'd picked out earlier, "after the fire, the earth is replenished." He instinctively knew that the release would bring a sense of renewal to his life.

****

Feeling lighter immediately after vomiting, Stephen lay back sprawling his arms out to the side and asked for joy. At that moment the black void burst to life as visions of the many people who love Stephen came into his awareness. His parents, his son, girlfriend, his close friends, friends from childhood.

They were all smiling, all there to support, all there to show him he's never alone. More and more people kept arriving at this party, cheers got louder, the colours brighter. Joy everywhere, just like he'd asked for.

Stephen didn't have to feel alone. He never was alone. He was always loved and only had to reach out for help, rather than shouldering the world's problems himself.

Much of the past year had been spent focusing on the painful fallout of his marriage break-up, the hurt it had caused, and fears about his young son's wellbeing following it all. He'd been beating himself up for the way he'd treated ex-partners too.

It was all solved in an instant. Mother Ayahuasca slid across his vision in the form of a snake, giving Stephen an important message.

She told him: "Look at your position in society. You have authority in your life and in your work, surrounded by women who look up to you and need your guidance.

"You have women all around you in your personal life: a beautiful girlfriend, ex-partner who is the mother of your son, your female relatives…be kind to these women. Nurture them, support them…and they will support you.

"Do not make me have to teach you this lesson again!", she warned him.

Stephen sat up with instant clarity over all the mistakes he'd been making. He knew he'd lacked the emotional maturity to understand that being kind to people, nurturing them and looking after them, pays dividends for you too.

He knew it wouldn't always be easy, but he must stick with that goal of treating the women in his life with kindness and respect.

He waved over Delilah and hugged her. He told her that he knew exactly what he needed to do.

Refusing another cup of ayahuasca, Stephen insisted: "I've got everything I came here for." The journey had ended and Stephen lay back on his mattress looking at the ceiling feeling excited, relieved, refreshed.

His thoughts wandered to hugging his girlfriend when he returned home to Scotland. To being more considerate to his ex partner and them working through past hurts to benefit their son.

Stephen said: "That moment with Mother Ayahuasca absolutely changed my life. Everything before had built up to that crucial lesson to treat others with respect and nurture the people close to you. Being more fulfilled by fulfilling other people.

"It has helped me move away from being self-centred, desire for instant gratification, the manipulation of people around me for my own ends. It has improved my relationships, in my personal life and in work.

"Before, there was a lot more conflict, selfishness, and not appreciating the good things I had in my life. I'm not saying that everything is now perfect because it's not.

"Mother Ayahuasca told me it wouldn't always be easy, but I need to stick with the mission. I don't want to feel the stern force of Mother Ayahuasca if I don't!"

That fourth ceremony was the most powerful. Everything in Stephen's life had been leading up to that understanding and change of direction.

He said: "It's all about kindness. The lesson was so simple but was beyond my comprehension. Treat the people in your life - women or men - with kindness. Nurture them and support them. If you do that then they will also nurture and support you.

"It seems so simple, but for someone who grew up usually having everything his own way, it has fundamentally shifted my field of vision.

"I'd previously always had this sense of entitlement. I should be entitled to that job, to that girl, to that experience…caught in a self-entitlement trap and self-absorbed in my own experience.

"Ayahuasca has opened my mind, unlocked the gates of consciousness, and allowed me to see inside myself. I still have some of the feelings and emotions that are attached to the old me but I'm far more aware of them - and the paths they lead to.

"I'm far more aware of my own behaviour, mind patterns, and it's much easier to manage that. You can drink ayahuasca and have amazing experiences, but the hard work really starts when you get home.

"You have a mission to put into practice and you don't simply change 35 years of behaviour overnight. It takes dedication to changing. Ayahuasca opens the gates…but you've got to walk the path."

CHAPTER 5

~

It's like I was given my life back

"I'll go to the Amazon jungle…if I make it through my senior year of university."

Anna Keppen made that promise to herself as her life dangled by a thread. She knew where she needed to go. She just didn't know whether or not she would live long enough to make it.

Aged 21, the student should have been happy, enjoying her best years, and full of excitement for many years ahead. Anna was none of those and feared she might not see her 22nd birthday.

Her body was weak, dangerously thin, and every meal she ate was puked up within minutes. The doctor had just diagnosed Anna with severe anaemia. For Anna, it was just another name added to the list on her medical file. Below it: bulimia, depression, anxiety…

The bulimia had taken over her body and the depression had numbed her mind. Anna felt utterly out of control. This was the person that only she knew. To everyone else, Anna was this smiling student with a 4.0 grade average at Southern Oregon University.

On the outside she was the happy-go-lucky yoga instructor preaching to people about health and consciousness. On the inside she was broken - and slowly dying.

"I knew it was going to kill me if I didn't do something drastic," explained Anna. "I knew there was a way out. I just couldn't find it in the Western world."

Anna's first real taste of Western medicine came 10 years earlier. She was in her doctor's office in her home town in Southern Oregon. Anna was sitting on the outside while her parents and the GP faced each other.

Anna was tired, uninterested and just wanted to be alone in her own bedroom. Her mum and dad were deep in conversation with the doctor, trying to figure out what was wrong. Looking to discover if they were doing something wrong.

Her mum, close to tears, said: "She's been very withdrawn for months now…and she's been unhappy for a long time. Not playing with friends or just doing what the other kids do. We're really worried."

The doctor nodded his head, in between scribbling some notes on the sheet of paper in front of him. Anna's parents were doing most of the talking, but within 15 minutes he had an answer. He could finally diagnose what was wrong with their daughter. The doctor gave his explanation in three simple words.

"Anna has depression," the doctor told her parents. "I realise she's still young, but she displays all the symptoms. I'll prescribe some medication and monitor her closely over the next few months."

Anna was officially on anti-depressants…at just 11 years old. For her parents, there was some relief and hope that the pills would revive their lost, inward child and put a smile back on her face. Anna just felt completely misunderstood.

The moment she swallowed the first pill, Anna immediately thought of her parents and doctor. She said to herself: "They don't know what to do with me - and the best thing they can do is give me this pill to try to make me better."

The longer she took the pills the more numb Anna felt. After six months she quit taking the anti-depressants, without asking her parents or her doctor. Even as a child, she instinctively knew they were doing her more harm than good.

Part of Anna had already been awakened to the idea that Western society is backwards. And she felt like she didn't fit in.

Anna said: "I'd always felt very disconnected from my family, from the American culture of drinking beer and watching football games, and where our main celebration is Christmas, where everyone buys each other artificial plastic shit, gets drunk…and expects to be happy.

"This is our sense of community and I never identified with it."

The broken child was part of a broken family. The more Anna's dad beat her mum up the more frightened Anna became. The screaming, the punches, blow after blow. Anna witnessed all of it.

She feared what was coming next and constantly thought of ways to keep her dad calm. Anything that might protect her mum.

****

Anna's parents divorced when she was aged 14, and three years later she also decided to go down her own path. Two weeks after high school graduation, Anna packed her bags and left the Republican, military kind of town she was brought up in.

She knew life had more to offer - and she certainly wasn't going to find it there.

When Anna was aged 13, there was one glimmer of hope when she visited an expert in Chinese medicine. Her parents had already tried everything in the Western approach, from counselling and all sorts of medical tests to the anti-depressants.

Yet the Chinese medicine man was the first person to get Anna's anxiety and heart rate under control using acupuncture.

That single session convinced Anna to go down the alternative path after she left home. She began studying health, education and native American studies in Southern Oregon University, focusing on alternative healing.

Lifting the cloud of depression was difficult enough, but bulimia followed and bit really hard as Anna progressed through her four year university course.

The yoga, the Chinese medicine, and everything she learned at university brought just a little relief from her body's pain and her mental warfare. Anna even apprenticed with a Native American, with the hope that their healing methods could rescue her.

In Spring of 2014, a series of coincidences stacked up that Anna couldn't ignore. Several surprise conversations with different people in less than a month, and suddenly another avenue of healing had appeared.

Anna explained: "I met five people completely randomly that talked to me about ayahuasca. One was in the grocery store, and one of them was in an airport. I began to think, 'okay, something is happening to me'.

"I got invited to five ayahuasca ceremonies. All of these people who had drunk ayahuasca had this passion and serenity, and had this brightness in their eyes, in their voice, and in their tone. That's what made me gravitate towards it.

"They were all inviting me to ceremonies in America but, from my training with Native Americans, I know it's always best to go to where the medicine comes from. That's why I said no to all those ceremonies and saved up to go to the Amazon instead.

"I told myself if I live through my senior year and I graduated I would save up and go to Peru. I was really honest with my family about what was going on and they supported me."

****

It was the summer of 2014 and Anna was aged 21 when she arrived at the Ananconda Cosmica ayahuasca retreat in Iquitos. They were deep in the jungle and the facilitators warned the group to be wary of six foot long poisonous snakes that sometimes jumped out of the leaves.

That warning set the tone and Anna was terrified as she was escorted to the large maloka that would be the setting for her first ayahuasca ceremony.

Chatting with the native shaman, Alvaro, Anna tried several ways of explaining why she was there. How desperate she was to lift the heavy depression from her back, how she longed to feel truly calm and centred for the first time in her life, and how to bury the bulimia that was plaguing her.

Anna had also brought some other baggage from North America to South America with her: deep resentment for her father.

She felt no love for him. Anna was too disgusted at how he could be so cruel to her mum. But all of that was put out of mind because Anna was still struggling to convey her list of medical problems to the shaman.

After each sentence Anna finished, the shaman still stared at her blankly. The facilitators tried their best to translate but sharing her issues had led to a pretty confusing conversation.

Then the shaman broke his silence. He leaned over to one of the facilitators, spoke a few words, and then smiled at Anna while looking directly into her eyes. The facilitator explained: "He said, 'don't worry, the medicine is going to do its work.'"

Anna sat on her mat staring outside into the darkness of the jungle. Her mind tried to run through different scenarios of what was to come, but those thoughts were quickly cut short. Anna quickly realised how pointless it was.

She knew where she would be voyaging - deep into her subconscious mind. But what she would discover was anyone's guess.

Around 15 people had spread round the edges of the maloka and shaman Alvaro walked round the circle, serving each person their drink. For Anna, it smelled like burnt molasses or coffee that had gone bad. But the taste was not quite as horrifying as expected.

Neither was her first journey. The whole night turned out to be gentle and soothing. Anna felt like Mother Ayahuasca was giving her an easy introduction because of her anxiety.

She got the message that was going to be okay, and that in upcoming ceremonies she'd be taken back to very old memories to help make her a better, more functional person.

Throughout the rest of her month-long trip, Anna drank ayahuasca every second night. Very intense, incredibly insightful, and all combining to give her real hope for change in her life. Of those 16 ceremonies, one stood out in particular.

Anna said: "I was really working through a lot of stuff with my dad, and feeling a lot of resentment towards him. Then ayahuasca all of a sudden transferred my 50 year old dad into a 10 year old boy.

"I saw his mother doing the same violent actions that he had done. Then I saw my grandmother as a 10 year old girl, and my great grandparents treating her the same way.

"Then I saw that all clearly that all these family members were only doing their best with what they'd been given.

"It was something I'd never considered before and it created this massive amount of compassion. Instead of fearing humanity or hating it, or being resentful for what may have happened, I saw that everybody was really just doing their best.

"And if we can learn how to be better, it will really change things for the next generation. That truly was one of my most transformative experiences ever. After a month of working intensively with the medicine, I worked on so many layers within myself and brought up so many memories from my subconscious mind.

"I found a lot of compassion for my family, specifically for my dad, and realised he was that way because he came from an entire generation that was very broken. That's really when my healing journey started."

****

Her journey has taken Anna down a long road over the past four years where she has participated in more than 200 ayahuasca and wachuma ceremonies. Anna has swapped North America for South America and now has Peruvian residency.

Aged 25, the American woman is now training to be a plant medicine apprentice and works as an ayahuasca facilitator at Aya Healing Retreats in the Amazon.

Guiding Anna is Don Miguel Lopez, a 43-year-old man who has been a shaman since he was 10-years-old. He is teaching her to work with the medicine in the tradition of the Shipibo tribe.

Anna also works alongside a family in the Andes who use the cactus plant medicine wachuma, better known as San Pedro, for healing.

On her first experience with ayahuasca, Anna and her shaman could barely understand each other. She now often does the translation for Westerners visiting Aya Healing Retreats, along with supporting participants throughout ceremonies, singing songs and icaros during the night.

The miraculous transformations she's witnessed have never failed to amaze Anna. One such case was the 63-year-old man who arrived with severe arthritis that forced him to give up his lifelong passion of cross country running. When he first came to the jungle he was overweight, not very mobile, and depressed about his condition.

Three weeks into his jungle trip, Anna came across him one day. She said: "He was sweating, he was smiling, and yelled at the top of his lungs, 'I just ran for the first time in 25 years'. He was crying and it was so beautiful to watch because running was his biggest passion and he never thought he'd be able to do it again.

"After working on the mental and emotional issues, which were really linked to the injuries he'd had, and the other combination of plant medicines he used, he was able to run again."

Anna also worked closely with an English woman who came to the jungle with a severe addiction to marijuana and was diagnosed with bipolar disorder. The woman had seemingly lost control of her mind, and her health was getting progressively worse back in Western society. Peru was a last throw of the dice.

Anna said: "After four weeks, ayahuasca and other plant medicines completely transformed her addiction. She went from walking in circles talking to herself - pretty much what people would call 'crazy' - to a completely normal, functional and beautiful human being.

"She's now writing a book about her experience. She's an amazing writer and an amazing person, but she needed plant medicine to clean up some of her issues. It was really powerful to see because I was with her the whole time."

In her own life, everything changed for the better for Anna. Healing her broken relationship with her father and grandmother finally brought the happiness and inner calm she'd been seeking since childhood. The depression and the eating disorder are long gone. Anna's the healthiest and happiest she's ever been.

Working through her trauma and changing her deeply held views of her father also resulted in something completely unexpected in the family.

Anna said: "My parents had been divorced for nearly 10 years, and I never thought in a million years they would get back together. But they started dating after I first came out of the Amazon and last year, after three years of dating, they got remarried.

"I attribute a lot of that to the medicine. When you do this internal work and there are shifts, it also shifts blockages for your family too. A huge part of my parents getting back together was definitely shifting that energy from resentment to compassion.

"And sharing these teachings with my family helped changed them too. They didn't even need to drink the medicine to change and heal."

While sitting with her shaman in the jungle one day, Anna asked him: "When does the healing stop?" He laughed, and replied: "We're functioning in a broken society. Healing is never going to stop. It's going to become easier, but until the world is whole and healed we'll keep using this energy for other people."

Her own experiences and shamanic teachings have shown Anna that the mental, physical and emotional issues are all just symptoms. The root cause is often broken relationships with our families and emotional wounds that have been passed on from generation to generation.

Anna said: "People will say, 'I need to heal my addiction', or 'I need to heal the tumour on my left breast', or 'I need to heal from a car accident I had last year'…and what my shaman says is that you 100% have to deal with the family stuff first.

"It's usually dealing with mum, dad, or significant events that happened as a child because patterns are created that become bigger and bigger. All of these patterns of really just trying to function and be a human manifest in backward ways of dealing with life.

"So you go back and address what happened, looking at it with compassion and transforming the energy from fear into love. Otherwise things won't change. The shamans will say you always have to go back to your family. That's the number one root cause of these issues.

"What happened when you were a child? What happened with your mum and dad? What happened when you were growing up?"

Ayahuasca uncovered why Anna was diagnosed with depression as a child. It manifested at the same time the violence began in her household. It got worse as her family began falling apart. A young girl looking for security, love and care instead found fear, loneliness and confusion.

Ayahuasca also clearly showed how the bulimia that followed was directly connected to the broken relationship with her father at that time.

She explained: "It started these patterns in me of seeking perfection. I thought that if I was perfect, maybe my dad will be less mad. That's what started the eating disorder for me and it was very intertwined with my depression.

"I thought that if my body is perfect, if I look perfect, then I'd be perfect and my dad would be less likely to get angry.

"That concept and thinking like that was with me all the way until I found ayahuasca. It led to a serious cycle of anxiety, depression, bulimia and trying to seek perfectionism. I thought that if I was perfect then the world would be easier.

"It sounds totally crazy but it was a 12 year old girl's perspective of trying to help dad be less mad, or lessen the trauma for mum. It was really trying to control a situation I had absolutely no control of."

Anna's parents were trying to piece their broken child back together, as was their doctor. They were all doing their best, and didn't know what else to do. Anne became so ill as an adult that she almost ran out of options too.

But she made it through that final year of university. She made it to Peru. The ayahuasca helped make her whole again.

"There's so much hope for people that they're unaware of because the Western medical world is running the show," said Anna. "Nobody is ever too far gone. There is always, always hope. I know that the world can change. Watching people go through these transformations, I know that we can do it as a society.

"I want to be of service and I want to help people the way I've been helped through the medicine. That's why I dived so deep working as an ayahuasca facilitator now because it has liberated so much for me.

"When I look at where I was, and photos of how I was, five years ago it almost makes me want to weep in gratitude. I owe that to these plant medicines. It's like I was given my life back."

CHAPTER 6

❧

My mind turned against me, but my soul is in charge

Throwing his rucksack quickly onto his back, Scott Fitzcharles rushed towards the front door so he wouldn't be late for the most important flight of his life.

Just as his left hand landed on the door knob, his mum grabbed his right forearm tightly and turned Scott to face her. They'd already chatted for hours in the lead up to his trip, but she had one more question to ask.

"What do you really expect to get from this?" she said, looking Scott straight in the eye. She was worried but didn't want him to know how much.

Scott replied: "I'm not my physical body, it's mine. I'm not my mind, it's mine. So where is me?

"I'm going to find where me is."

It was the end of April, 2017, and Scott headed for Toronto International Airport with his dad. Destination - Iquitos, Peru. Two flights, a 16 hour trip from North to South America, and a week-long stay deep in the Amazon jungle drinking ayahuasca.

The 41-year-old arrived at the Kapitari retreat on Monday lunchtime. The traditional, rustic-looking retreat was all very familiar. From the huge circular maloka where he would be drinking the medicine to the tambo where he would be sleeping at night, Scott had seen just about every inch of the place through videos he'd watched countless times online.

The day began with a group meeting, then each person was called for a one-on-one with the shaman Don Lucho and translators. "Why are you here?" they asked Scott. He'd already explained in the online questionnaire that he was losing a fight with depression. He shared his problem once again face-to-face.

The meeting was quickly over and Scott was instructed to be at the maloka that night at 7p.m. for the first of four ayahuasca ceremonies that week.

Stepping inside the circular hut at 6.45p.m., Scott looked up and all around at the huge expansive maloka. It was 14 metres across so each of the 13 participants had plenty of personal space.

Scott picked his spot and sat down where a yoga mat, pillow, thin blanket, and some toilet paper had been set out for him. A sick bucket also sat to the right hand side of his mat.

Shaman Don Lucho arrived at 7p.m. sharp along with his son. Both sat at the back centre of the maloka and would take turns in singing icaros, while two facilitators kept an eye on proceedings.

Scott was very calm, in fact, he was raring to go. He sprang up to his feet when he was called forward to drink ayahuasca for the first time.

The brown liquid was served in a small shot glass for every participant just after 7p.m. Then the candle went out.

It was pitch black in the maloka, with only the moon dictating how much light appeared in the ceremonial space.

For the first hour Scott sat with his legs crossed thinking about family, friends and past experiences. All of it positive, a blissful type feeling. Scott felt comfortable and giggled to himself in the darkness, but couldn't truly relax as he'd built himself up so much for the retreat.

At 9p.m. one of the facilitators asked Scott if he felt dizzy or sick, and if he wanted to drink again. Within 30 seconds of downing his second shot, Scott's mind began plotting how he could convince them to give him a third drink of ayahuasca.

It was like his alcoholic days all over again. Scott was always greedy, drinking until the booze ran out - or he passed out. He'd quit drinking alcohol years earlier, but in Peru the habit of greediness resurfaced in a big way.

Scott could feel the medicine working subtly inside, but he wanted to go deeper. He expected more from it. Walking back from the bathroom, a facilitator grabbed Scott's shoulder and whispered in his ear: "Do you feel the medicine?".

Scott replied: "Yes, but it's not too strong. It's mild." It wasn't exactly mild, but Scott was trying to lay the groundwork for drink number three.

Sitting back down, Scott went back into the zone of thinking positive thoughts about his family and friends. The sound of icaros continued for two hours without break. Don Lucho and his son were alternating between singing to maintain continuity throughout the ceremony.

But just after the halfway point, Don Lucho made his way out of the maloka, treading quietly so as not to disturb the group. But Scott watched his every move, from leaving the maloka to putting on his head torch and wandering into the jungle.

The shaman was bouncing around in the darkness outside, like a firefly, as Scott kept his eyes firmly on him from inside the maloka.

Suddenly Scott knew what was happening - and where the shaman was going.

"They've given us a watered down version of ayahuasca, just to gauge how everyone reacts" he said to himself. "Now he's going to get the real stuff."

For months before arriving in Peru, Scott had watched countless videos where people were talking about the spirit connected with ayahuasca. He still didn't know if he believed any of it.

Don Lucho trudged back pushing through the leaves, with his head torch leading a path back to the maloka. Just as the shaman switched off the head torch outside, Scott said to himself once again: "That's him back with the good stuff."

But the moment Don Lucho re-entered the maloka, that's when the medicine took complete control. Having casually sat up all night, Scott had to lie down - before he fell down.

His head was dizzy and his body was weak, but Scott could feel a strong energy inside the maloka. He couldn't see it, but could really feel it swirling around the maloka above everyone's heads.

It all began to make sense. Scott said to himself: "He didn't go away and get the good stuff...he brought back the spirit with him. She's here."

The energy hovered around inside the room. Whenever it came near Scott, it created a rippling effect, like the wake from a boat. After a few minutes, Scott sat back up again, trying to figure out what was going on and locate the energy.

It quite quickly turned into a bright white light that was swirling around the room. The 14ft long solid logs in the roofspace of the maloka began moving and bending. Scott began studying the moving bright light again, and then glanced over at the others convinced that they must have been as blown away as he was.

Scott explained: "When I was looking around the room at the silhouettes of everyone, the light would reappear brightly at each person. It was flashing on each of them in the room, one by one.

"It was going real slow and then I realised - that's their heart. Each flash of the light was the person's heartbeat. Then it moved onto the next person, and the next. As it came around the room towards me, my mind turned to, 'what's this gonna do when it reaches me?'

"When the light came to me it disappeared. It was like I was standing in the sea up to my waist, then a wave comes and catches you off guard. It was like a small wave that hit had me. I was blown away with it. I immediately looked to my right again, and the light just kept going."

As the light kept circling the room, Scott stared at it more intently and then began to control it. He made it go faster, slower, and then made it reverse. Next he tried to make it change colour, but couldn't. It remained a bright white light until the ayahuasca wore off.

Two and a half years earlier in Canada, Scott had quit boozing following a 20 year alcohol addiction. Without alcohol, life was supposed to get better. Without daily drinking, he would have freedom and really begin to enjoy life. That was the idea, but the opposite happened.

Scott moved back to Scotland and his world became increasingly difficult. Walking out of jobs. Finding it really hard to function each day. Being drunk was like a mask he used to hide behind - and he didn't have it anymore.

When life used to get on top of him, Scott would simply go and get drunk. Without alcohol, Scott spiralled into negativity and a sense of hopelessness that the doctor told him was "depression".

His ex-wife's depression was what had killed their relationship. It was one of the root reasons he hadn't seen their 12-year-old son since he was a toddler. And after finally quitting drinking after two decades, depression was seemingly haunting Scott once again.

But sitting in his doctor's office, Scott insisted there was much more going on.

He told his doctor: "I'm not arguing with your diagnosis here, but I truly think that that's not the problem. I see the depression as being a symptom of something else, or something larger. It's not just depression.

"If you want to just quit the exploration at depression and treat the depression, then I'm not interested. And I'm certainly not interested in the pills."

For years, Scott had witnessed his ex-wife being prescribed various anti-depressants and seen how the pills worked temporarily, and then stopped working altogether. He'd seen first hand the damage they caused to his ex-wife and their relationship.

After visiting doctors in Canada and Scotland, both of them came up with anti-depressants as a solution to his problems. Scott didn't want any part in it.

Fifteen years earlier, Scott had first heard of ayahuasca while watching a TV documentary. The medicine was being used as an addiction therapy, and Scott watched as it documented people successfully coming off heroin.

It never crossed his mind again because he thought it was a treatment for drug addicts.

Still struggling to cope with life in Scotland after quitting alcohol, Scott reached out to one of his oldest friends in Canada on Facebook.

He wrote: "I don't know what to do. I'm losing it again! Life's not making sense, I'm getting pissed off with everything."

His friend responded with one suggestion after another. Scott had either tried it all before and got nowhere. Frustrated, fed-up, and angry, a thought suddenly appeared in Scott's head. He quickly sent it in a message to his friend…

He wrote: "Dude, I've tried fucking everything. What I need is ayahuasca!"

Ayahuasca had just come into his head from nowhere. Scott hadn't heard anything about it, read a word about it, or even thought about ayahuasca once since watching the TV programme 15 years earlier. It just filtered into his mind in that moment of need.

It sounded like a random, throw-away comment but to Scott this was no coincidence. Those drug addicts in the documentary he'd watched were struggling, desperate and helpless. So was he.

Scott knew it was time to listen up and take action. He consumed every article he could find on ayahuasca, watched every online video possible, and began researching places to drink the medicine around the world.

His intuition had told him he needed ayahuasca - and Scott decided to pay attention to his gut feeling once again in order to choose the right ayahuasca retreat. He trawled website after website, but each time he felt a strong pull towards Kapitari.

It was a retreat near Iquitos in Peru, led by a shaman who had been practising with ayahuasca for 50 years.

There was one problem - a news report flashed up about a death at Kapitari in 2015. A 24-year-old backpacker had died there after drinking tobacco tea, failing to purge the drink, and it poisoned him.

Despite this, something kept pulling Scott towards Kapitari and the shaman Don Lucho. Within six months, Scott was at Kapitari for a week-long retreat consisting of four ayahuasca ceremonies.

After his first night of drinking ayahuasca and witnessing the light energy hovering around the maloka, Scott knew that travelling to Peru was one of the best decisions of his life. Some of the others in the group were a little apprehensive and stunned by what had happened, but Scott was very excited about what was to come in ceremony two.

****

A group-sharing circle was held earlier in the day where everyone spoke about their first night. Hearing other people's deep experiences gave Scott an even greater appreciation of the inner work being done at Kapitari.

As ceremony two got underway at 7p.m., each person sat in front of the shaman one by one to drink the medicine. When Scott kneeled on the floor, he was asked by one of the facilitators, "do you want to drink more?"

He replied "yes" and the medicine was served in a larger shot glass, which was double the dose from the previous night. Holding the glass in his hands and closing his eyes, Scott thought of his intention for the night's journey.

"Show me love," he said to himself, before drinking.

For the first couple of hours, Scott sat calmly without any nausea or purging and had an internal dialogue going on. He pondered over his relationship with the son he hadn't seen for years.

Despite the hurt and worry over the situation, the thoughts were all positive. The evening moved onto self-praise, an unfamiliar theme in Scott's life.

He gave himself a pat on the back for quitting drinking alcohol, he praised himself for never once getting arrested when heated arguments flared up with his ex-wife, and for taking positive steps to heal himself.

It became clear that Scott had never really praised himself or properly appreciated the positive aspects of his life. He was always too consumed with his perspective that life was not getting better. Too consumed with the next problem.

The second shot of ayahuasca came at 9p.m. and, soon after, Scott realised that a bug outside in the wilderness was singing in harmony with the shaman. In perfect timing at the end of every line in the song, the bug would pipe up with its distinctive "meep" noise.

And as he lay down on his yoga mat, Scott was confronted by another bug. Only this one was the size of a human being, and was stood upright directly in front of him.

The giant ant had a turtle shell on its back, and was wearing a World War One-style tin helmet. The angry ant was holding a machine gun - and pointing it directly at Scott.

He stared right back, afraid to look left or right in case it broke the connection. The ant never opened its mouth to speak, but it somehow sent the message, "you're just as simple as me." Then it disappeared.

Scott explained: "It was unbelievable. Before the ceremony was over I understood that message to mean that I was complicating life - and I didn't have to. I was always making life more difficult than it needed to be. The problems I was having were all self made."

Despite this important lesson, Scott felt low and disappointed the following day. He'd asked for Mother Ayahuasca to show him love. He wanted to know what it felt like for real, but she didn't deliver.

Then came a powerful insight later in the day: he'd spent the whole night showing himself love. Praising himself for the first time in years, acknowledging his achievements, developing his self-worth.

Scott said: "Mother Ayahuasca didn't show me love, she wasn't going to. But she showed me how to love myself. In conjunction with the ant teaching me about how I need to stop complicating life unnecessarily, I was also shown that I need to start loving myself."

In the two ceremonies that followed, he drank even more hoping to get more from the experience. It never turned out that way, and Scott felt like he'd wasted those final two ceremonies by being greedy and trying to control events. Yet when he returned home the impact on his life was huge.

Nothing miraculous happened in his life back home, but Scott was surprised to find himself much more calm. He took his time to make decisions and the anger that usually surfaced whenever he encountered a problem had disappeared.

The depression - it was gone. Day to day, Scott had a more positive energy rather than the negative energy that had always pulled him down.

Scott and three friends returned to Kapitari on the one year anniversary of their first retreat. They were joined by 17 newcomers, and Scott's approach this time was to drink less than before and allow events to unfold as organically as possible.

For ceremony one, Scott went in purposely with no intention. Just happy to be there, to reconnect, and with no expectations.

The effects of the medicine kicked in quickly and, as the journey progressed, Scott developed an intention. Lying on the floor and looking up into the darkness of the maloka, he said to himself: "I wanna meet you - and I wanna meet me."

Glancing down his body, Scott had a vision of wearing a hip pouch. As he stared down, it slowly opened to reveal Canadian coins. Seconds later Scott was flying through the air over the rocky mountains in Canada.

He'd never been to that part of Canada, but was mesmerised by the beauty of the landscape. The flying journey continued to his home town just outside Toronto, spotting parks and places where he used to hang out as a teenager.

Gliding over the CN Tower, and all along the Toronto waterfront, Scott felt an amazing feeling of love for Canada. The country was good to Scott for so long - but this was him saying goodbye.

He got the message that his life didn't have to be a revolving door of living between Canada and Scotland. He's been switching between both countries every six months or so when times got tough, but he needed to be with his partner and stepson in Scotland.

Returning his focus to his intention, Scott said to himself, "I want to meet you". Looking at the top of the maloka he saw a figure hiding behind the logs. As he looked closer, it vanished. No matter how hard he focused, he had no success in contacting Mother Ayahuasca.

Instead, Scott switched to the second part of his intention, "I wanna meet me." Immediately, he was shown a photograph that was in his living room back home. A picture of Scott and his brother where he was best man at his brother's wedding five years earlier.

Staring at the picture, it began to change into another image. One that doesn't exist. Scott saw himself as the groom this time - and his stepson Daniel as his best man.

The photograph disappeared and Scott found himself sitting in a tree looking down on himself and his stepson, having a conversation. Listening in closely, Scott heard Daniel say: "You are my dad." He replied: "And you are my son," before the pair embraced.

He'd gone back and forth to Canada for years searching for something, and Scott realised it was all an illusion. He'd asked to meet himself - and was being shown his family in Scotland. His partner and stepson loved him, supported him, and missed him whenever he left for Canada.

No matter his struggles, they welcomed Scott back every time with open arms. Why keep searching for himself when his life is in Scotland with them?

Two more ayahuasca ceremonies followed, but nothing came close to the huge lesson he had that night. The first retreat had given him the power to manage himself better every day and stay positive, along with jigsaw pieces for putting his life back together again. The second provided clarity and instructions on how to complete the puzzle.

Living in Scotland with his partner and stepson, Scott has been depression free for the past 16 months since his first ayahausca retreat. The doctor didn't have the answers and neither did the anti-depressants. The medicine helped Scott discover the answers himself.

He said: "Self-love is the key to everything. I was going to continue to suffer in many, many different aspects of my life - until I discovered that self-love.

"Mother Ayahuasca made me aware that I have a soul, I have a spirit. Once I recognised and acknowledged that spirit, it's now on my side guiding me now. All I had to do was show my self love for it to reawaken.

"All I know for sure is that having learned my lessons through ayahuasca, I'm a better person for it. I present myself as my best self to every situation or person I meet. I previously tried to think my way out of all the tough situations in life. It overloaded my mind and my mind turned against me.

"Before leaving for Peru I told my mum I was not my mind or body, and I was going to find me. What I've found is that I am my soul...and that is the most beautiful thing."

CHAPTER 7

~

I was birthing...rebirthing myself

Finola Foley staggered in the ceremony room and lay down in case she passed out...just like the day before.

The pain in her lower abdomen was excruciating. It came in frequent waves, feeling stronger each time.

Sweat gathered on her forehead as tears filled her eyelids. Rosie and Bernardine knelt beside her on the floor, holding her hands and talking Finola through it.

A few of the comforting words went in, most didn't. Every piece of energy Finola had was directed towards fighting the pain, trying to get through it.

"Stop the pain, stop the pain" she screamed through the tears after another jolt shot into her stomach.

Rewind more than 30 years and that's where the stomach pains all began. While her teenage friends were simply uncomfortable when they first began menstruating, for Finola it was hellish.

The stomach pains were so overwhelming she would pass out. Every time. Every month. This continued throughout the Irish woman's teenage years and through her marriage.

It was a medical mystery. Finola visited every top specialist in Ireland, praying that the next one would have the answer. They didn't. She was told keyhole surgery may be the answer. It wasn't.

After 25 years the pain became bearable and the blackouts stopped happening when she worked with energy healer David Lynch. While she continued to work as a pharmaceutical operator, becoming an energy healer was also her calling. David told her so.

His spiritual growth helped ease the pain of a rough divorce. The energy work and helping others with their problems also helped Finola come to terms with her mum's death. She directed her life by asking questions through prayer and waiting for the answers.

This time it was a Wednesday night, January 17, 2018. Finola asked an unusual question this time…about psychedelic medicine. The previous year, she was ill more often than she was well. Finola was drained and was desperate just to feel physically healthy again.

"I had caught every virus that was going around," she said. "I live a healthy life, I eat healthy food, and so I had no idea why this kept happening to me. I was sick to death of being sick. A few months earlier,

I'd also hurt my foot and it had been a bad injury. It affected my posture and had thrown me off balance."

As she sat patiently in her kitchen chair, words flowed into her mind that couldn't have been clearer.

"It's my gift to me to heal my mind, body, soul and spirit. It's my reason for being here. My soul is calling me to do this work."

Finola said: "I was surprised and I thought, 'this is profound - I'd better write this down'".

With a retreat taking place in a few weeks' time, Finola felt a strong pull towards the medicine. She booked up for three ayahuasca ceremonies, three kambo sessions, and one experience of bufo.

"The kambo in particular called out to me," said Finola. "I needed physical healing and it reportedly wards off 1500 diseases and is used in the Amazon as a vaccination for the year. I set out with the intention for complete physical healing. Everything was about removing the pain and healing the body."

****

Finola sat on the floor to drink her first cup of the ayahuasca brew. She had no fear of what was to come. She felt safe in her heart and was confident that this set would protect her through the journey.

She was right. She travelled through a bright, colourful space and was gently pulled into a psychedelic dimension. Soon she was asked, "who are you?" Did she really know who she was? Was she living up to her true potential?

As she continued along the colourful, peaceful journey, two sign-posts appeared. They were white with black writing. They looked just like the ones you would see on a motorway.

The sign-posts challenged Finola about her belief systems. Her family came from a Church Of Ireland background and Finola had converted to Catholicism after getting married in 1988.

Finola said: "I believe I was shown that I needed to challenge these religious belief systems and get a hold of them. I felt that Mother Ayahuasca was taking care of me. I'm a very spiritual person. I feel very grounded and have a close connection to Jesus.

"I've been through a painful divorce, lost my mum, had a lot of challenges in my life. But I've always felt safe and managed to overcome them."

While the ayahuasca medicine allowed Finola to experience an emotional detox, it appeared that the kambo medicine did the opposite of healing her physical problems.

On day two, the frog poison was placed onto five small burn spots on Finola's arm. She purged almost immediately. Then again, several more times. The taste in her mouth was rancid, toxic…just like the day before. Only this time she didn't become unconscious for a few minutes.

Instead, Finola felt a sudden rush to her left foot and intense stabbing pain. She reacted by lifting her left leg in the air, wincing in agony. She screamed in pain, but it continued.

Rosie, one of the facilitators, leaned over and gave Finola a dose of the shamanic snuff rape to try and ease her pain. It subsided but she couldn't walk. A group of others at the retreat carefully picked her up and carried Finola to her room.

It seemed that her foot injury from eight months earlier had flared up again. An hour later, she real source of the pain came into her mind. This was a foot injury she'd suffered nine years earlier while on holiday in Machu Pichu. Back then, it was hurriedly bandaged up so she could continue with the rest of her trip.

It had never truly healed, and had now spontaneously returned screaming for attention. For proper healing this time around.

Finola said: "Your feet are about moving forward - and sometimes we are afraid of moving forward in life. If you don't do what you are meant to do sometimes you experience pain. This physical injury had come back to be relived and healed so I could properly move on."

Just five tiny applications of the frog poison had turned Finola's left foot black and blue with bruising and swelling. She hobbled around her room. She then sat down on her bed and couldn't even lift it onto the mattress.

Finola would need to be carried back to the ceremonial space in the evening, otherwise she would miss out on ayahuasca ceremony number two. Drinking the second cup, Finola set her intention for physical healing once again. As she got her second taste of the medicine, Finola was not expecting what happened next.

She lay down on the floor and let the medicine settle in her system. Again it felt gentle, and Finola was calm as she tuned into the background music.

"It took about 30 minutes before I could feel anything happening," she said. "Then suddenly I got a huge pain in my left foot again. It was a shooting pain in the same area from earlier. About 10 minutes later I could feel it lifting and actually leaving my body.

"All the medicines were working together to heal my foot. It was profound. It was like a miraculous physical healing and I've never experienced anything like it. I had originally thought this injury was from eight months earlier and was shown I'd carried it from nine years ago. Then the pain just left me completely that night.

"I could hardly even stand up on it an hour earlier. The pain was killing me and I was hobbling around. I'm very spiritual and open to anything. I've had strange experiences of people touching me on the shoulder - and nobody is there.

"I've had spirits come to me. But this was incredible...you wouldn't imagine something like that could happen."

Finola's journey continued that night with a free spirit theme where she felt connected with Mother Earth. She saw a beautiful scene of trees that were coloured grey and white. She merged with them, becoming the branches and feeling at peace.

It became a dance of freedom for her. She was free of worry. Free of concerns. Free of pain...until her third and final experience with kambo the following day.

"Mummmm!" she screamed once again. Lying on the floor with Rosie and Bernardine by her side, Finola lifted her legs up onto the table.

The stomach pains surged in at more regular intervals...like contractions. There was no bump in her stomach. No baby inside. She'd never given birth before.

Aged 49 and lying in agony on the floor, she then knew what labour was like. Rosie and Bernardine were like her midwives offering support as the kambo worked through her body and released the stuck energy that had plagued her for 30 years.

"It felt like I was birthing…but rebirthing myself," she said.

After two hours the pain subsided and Finola burst into tears. Rosie and Bernardine hugged her, smiling with admiration at how she had come through it.

"Mummmm", cried out Finola. Her mum, Mary O'Neill, had died nine years earlier but was immediately in her thoughts as she let go of past hurt and blockages with this incredible rebirthing experience.

Later that evening Finola was sitting calmly in front of Arron, one of the retreat facilitators. "I want you to repeat after me…'I am beautiful'," said Arron.

Finola followed. In a shallow voice, with no energy behind it. Her body began to tense up as she sat facing him in the candlelit ceremony room.

Three simple words. Yet it felt so hard.

Arron asked her to do the same again… "this time from the heart," he said. Finola's lips moved but the rest of her body resisted. It didn't feel natural.

That short practice reawakened what Finola already knew - that she didn't love herself enough. She knew instantly what her intention would be for her third and final ayahuasca ceremony at the retreat.

She asked Mother Ayahuasca to help her see her true beauty, and to clear away the self-criticism or negative comments she'd held onto for too long.

As the medicine worked through Finola, she saw herself as a snowflake. Floating softly in her own mind, Finola saw her uniqueness. Her individual beauty.

It became clear that it was only her ego that wouldn't allow her to be beautiful. Yet God makes everything beautiful.

"I found it very hard to accept that I am beautiful, said Finola. "That gave the me focus to do some work around this in my final ceremony. It's very hard when you do love yourself, but you really need to love yourself more.

"We are all very hard on ourselves, but I love who I am in my soul. I used to get bogged down by how I thought people perceived me. Some people can be mean-spirited. Of course we are all beautiful. We just have to learn to accept ourselves as being beautiful."

Finola is continuing with her spiritual energy work, and her painful experiences over three days allowed her to heal a wound that was trapped within for decades.

The medicines, ayahuasca, kambo, and bufo, worked together to bring about this healing. Unlike the experiences of many others, Finola's ayahuasca journeys were were gentle and she was guided through them with ease.

She said: "I also set my intention not to let fear in, only love. If you talk to yourself and Mother Ayahuasca with love there is nothing to be afraid of."

CHAPTER 8

~

They call the real medicine drugs, and the drugs medicine

Nicolette Van Der Waal sat across from Jan Bartelsman desperate for answers.

Answers on what to do next. Where her career should take her. Clues about what her purpose was in life.

She was a 45-year-old therapist feeling lost and in need of direction. He was an astrologer who did soul horoscope readings, and had shown countless people what their purpose on earth is. Jan is also a shaman and had long been using entheogens as a method of healing.

It was 2006 and they were sitting facing each other in Jan's home. He lived in an ordinary house in Leiden, a city in the province of South Holland known for its centuries-old architecture and having the country's oldest university.

Jan was wise, kind, down to earth, and was clear in his conversation with Nicolette. She would continue working as a therapist and counsellor, but her work would go far beyond this as a healer, Jan told her. To get to this stage Nicolette would have to work on herself first with plant medicines.

He said: "You can go into therapies for another 10 years, but if you want healing on a deep level, drink ayahuasca."

Jan advised Nicolette to visit the Santo Daime Church, of which he was a member, and gave her the website address. She looked it up online, saw people dancing and singing Portuguese hymns - and apparently taking drugs.

"No way, not for me," she thought.

Six months later, Nicolette was in France learning about breathwork and bodywork to develop her career as a therapist. The teacher insisted that to be a great therapist helping other people then first you have to know your own depths, and what issues you have still to overcome.

"The best way to do that is drink ayahuasca," said her teacher. Ayahuasca was on her path - again. Twelve people in the group agreed to drink ayahuasca with the teacher at the end of the week. She'd received the medicine from the Santo Daime Church which has permission to use ayahausca as a sacrament and the teacher, along with two guides, supported Nicolette through a rough night.

Nicolette said: "My first experience was not a pleasant one. I was in a very dark place and had the experience of my own birth again, and how I'd come to earth in fear of being here.

"I was really upset and thought that I'd never drink ayahausca again, but this was my first step on my path towards healing. The next day I felt so good, that something had definitely lifted from me. I knew because of the medicine that something inside had healed and I wanted to do it again."

For Nicolette life was okay. A mother of two grown-up daughters, she had a full-time job counselling other people. No serious trauma, or depression, or addiction, like many of the others seeking help through ayahuasca. Yet each time she drank the medicine it pulled another problem she wasn't aware of from her subconscious mind that had been influencing her everyday life.

As a therapist Nicolette was fascinated by how humans functioned. In her last job as a nurse in a mental hospital, she was intrigued by psychology and getting inside other people's heads. Always trying to figure out how things could go wrong with people mentally.

It was time to properly explore her own psyche. She'd landed on a spiritual path unexpectedly and decided to just start walking. She joined the Santo Daime Church in Holland, then trips to Brazil and Peru followed. Cup after cup of ayahuasca, working through layers of fears and blockages that had been holding Nicolette back from experiencing her own freedom.

Her adult life had been spent trying to make other people happy...to feel safe. Working in jobs that were not meant for her...but that seemed secure. Mental programmes and behavioural patterns repeating...all used as a shield in her inner battle with fear.

Journeys with the medicine kept showing Nicolette how fearful she was. Locked into her nervous system. At the root of physical problems in her body. Driving her daily patterns and choices in life.

That first cup came at the age of 45. Dozens more followed as Nicolette threw away the shield and transformed those fears. As a middle-aged woman, she finally became acquainted with who she really is.

She walked away from a relationship that wasn't good for her. Walked away from trying to please everyone. Walked towards herself instead.

She left behind old destructive behaviours. Left behind a life in Ireland to move back home to Holland. Left behind a draining job and took on a new challenge.

She said: "I reshaped my old life that was based on fear. I created my own life again by doing the things that I wanted to do. Before, my whole life was based on safety. It was a really tough road but it has been transformative for me."

****

Following her trips to Peru and Brazil, Nicolette learned more about the medicine and her connection with Mother Ayahuasca grew. Four years on, it was time to take the next steps on her path - brewing the medicine and starting her own ceremonies.

It all fell into place as she united with fellow facilitators Ellie and Gerard at the Mens en Aandacht retreat, a beautiful spot in the countryside in the south of the Netherlands. The perfect centre for healing within an old rectory building surrounded by forest. Their mission: to guide people on their journey of waking up to who they really are.

For the past six years, up to five guides at Mens en Aandacht have supported and cared for hundreds of people from all over the world. Groups of 14 people every other weekend, and week-long ceremonies for six or seven weeks per year.

The retreat is often fully booked six months in advance. They never have to advertise or promote what they do. Word of mouth naturally spreads as the people whose lives have been completely renewed bring in their partners, relatives, friends. The medicine organically spreads across Europe one person at a time.

The loving guides have been watching in amazement as people sleepwalking through life wake up more rapidly…in as little as two or three ceremonies. All due to a global shift in consciousness, according to Nicolette.

She said: "The shifts people are making now are quicker than 10 years ago. When I started 12 years ago there weren't as many people doing this work, and the work was also hidden because it was illegal and not understood by the majority of people. We were progressing slowly.

"Even though the shamans have been working with ayahuasca for thousands of years, in the West not many people were doing this work. A lot of work is personal, but much of it is also collective. When I'm transforming my fear I'm also transforming the fear of my mother and grandmother, and I'm transforming it for my children.

"When we drink ayahuasca we are lifting all these negative emotions from the collective consciousness. You are doing your personal work, but also collective work too. It's all connected.

"If I look at people who drink ayahuasca now, the younger generation in their 20s and 30s, it's amazing to see where they are. I was in my forties when I started making progress with ayahausca - and they are already there. The collective consciousness is shifting so quickly and there's got to be a time where we go past the point of no return.

"Mother Ayahuasca is often described as a snake who has been hidden in the jungle for a long time. Now she's spreading all over the world."

Returning to Peru in May 2017 was another learning experience for Nicolette. She watched as the shamans made the brew and worked with it amongst their own people and the many visitors flooding places like Iquitos to experience the medicine in its home location.

Those traditional ceremonies didn't have the same therapeutic qualities as back home in the Netherlands. There was less focus on integrative work and after-care following deep, and often confusing, experiences.

These indigenous people live a completely different life in the jungle. Connected with spirit, while our connection is broken. Less temptation, addictions, stress, materialism, chaos…while these create a constant struggle in our Western societies.

We don't fully understand their cultural problems, they don't fully get ours. Nicolette insisted that this underlines the importance of European facilitators continuing their important work. Guiding people home in a safe setting that's literally closer to home.

In the past six years, Nicolette, Ellie and Gerard have witnessed what they consider miracles through ayahuasca. A woman diagnosed with breast cancer was cured after all the negativity and stress was removed from her life following her ayahuasca journeys.

Another woman in her late 20s, who had suffered depression for 15 years and had not responded to any kind of medication, psychotherapy, and countless other alternative treatments. The depression finally lifted after just two ayahausca sessions and she continued to live a happy, normal life long afterwards.

Men and women would leave addictions behind and healing childhood trauma wounds every week. As a counsellor and plant medicine facilitator, Nicolette is in the perfect position to compare standard Western methods of treatment for deep psychological and emotional issues with the traditional plant medicine remedies brought here from the Amazonian jungle.

She said: "You can talk a lot with people, for many years, but there's always projection. With talking there's always the ego, defence mechanisms that keep you from telling the truth about yourself, your emotions and your thoughts.

"With ayahuasca you are your own therapist and you come into dimensions within yourself that you could never reach just by talking. There's no-one in between and it works the fastest way. You could never achieve the same result talking with people.

"With ayahuasca, it shows you so clearly what you do with your thoughts, emotions and your behaviour. I don't know of anything beyond psychedelics and entheogens that allow you to go so deep and do this inner work.

"Psychedelics, like psilocybin, MDMA, frog medicine such as kambo, plant medicines, are emerging as powerful healers and are spreading quickly. But I would like to see the plant medicines get more attention. There's been a lot of scientific research done on ayahuasca but it never shows up anywhere.

"They call the real medicine drugs, and the drugs medicine. Everything is upside down."

CHAPTER 9

◡

The importance of learning to be yourself

Gohar Khan glanced over at his camera and felt guilty for not living up to his promise.

He'd told his friends he would do a photoshoot for them, but was now avoiding them.

"I don't think they'll really like my work," the young photography student said to himself. "What if I mess this one up?"

In one click of his mind, the photoshoot was cancelled. The mental battle quickly over. Self-criticism 1 - 0 creativity.

As a child growing up in Pakistan, Gohar loved making music, drawing, allowing his creative side to shine. The arts lit him up and led to him eventually studying film at a university in Orlando, USA.

Yet there he was sitting in his student apartment staring vacantly at his camera. His fear and a sense of inadequacy were blocking him from expressing himself and following his passion for photography. Same old story: start a project and then quit early because the inner critic said so. His self-confidence on the floor.

Gohar looked into the camera lens and didn't like the reflection staring back at him. Twenty years old, weighing 340lbs, isolated indoors voluntarily.

It was easier being locked away from the outside world. No people-pleasing. No anxiety. No maintaining the fake act that he was becoming increasingly uncomfortable with.

Gohar felt confused. Inauthentic. Living a life that didn't feel like his own. Instead, he'd created a character through mental programmes from childhood, influences from family and friends around him, and what the media and society expected of young men.

His escape? Stuffing more junk food down his throat to stuff down his negative emotions. Playing video games and watching TV all day long to stay distracted. Jumping from one fake reality to another. His life rotting away indoors.

"I was someone who would say yes to a lot of stuff, even if I didn't necessarily want to," said Gohar. "I was not comfortable being myself and it felt like I was walking on eggshells just to please other people.

"I also had a lot of inner criticisms that stopped me from doing a lot of things. Self-doubt often held me back. I'd fallen into a creative block and just as I'd want to start anything the inner criticism and doubts would appear. So instead I'd self-medicate by watching TV all day, playing video games, eating junk food. I had no compassion for other people and for what I was going through."

It was December 2017 and Gohar made one of few trips outside of his apartment...to attend an ayahuasca retreat at a secret farm location. For him this was just to be another form of escapism. Naively more interested in the psychedelic effects than the healing potential of the Amazonian brew.

A group of around 20 people gathered in a circle in the ceremonial space. Gohar sat cross-legged on his mat gazing at the hanging dream catchers and colourful ceremonial decorations. The facilitators asked the group to have their intentions in mind for the evening.

A pot mixture of herbs sat in the middle of the room. This was used for energy cleansing and each person rubbed the liquid on their hands and face in preparation for the ayahuasca.

Shortly after drinking his first cup of the medicine, it lifted feelings of anxiety within Gohar to the surface. He pulled his blanket more tightly over his head. The tension and tightness kept building but eventually reached a point of release - and openness. This wasn't like letting go; it was like a heavy negative load being pulled from his body.

It was beautiful. Gohar cried, with bursts of laughter in between. Getting louder as he felt progressively lighter.

Gohar's right hand raised up - without any mental instruction behind it. He began patting his own head in a comforting way, feeling a motherly presence around him. Thoughts of problems he had with his parents when he was younger floated into his awareness, but it was all okay. This felt like home. Comfort, attention, so much love.

"Could you please be a bit quieter?" one of the facilitators whispered in Gohar's ear. He was laughing so loud, enjoying every second of the experience.

Apologising…Gohar then began saying sorry to himself. Over and over. Sorry for the self-criticism. Sorry for neglecting himself. Sorry for always beating himself up.

"Then I started getting these flashbacks of traumatic events from childhood," said Gohar. "I was living through that again and feeling all those emotions that I had not really acknowledged before. It was so good to process these energies and let go of them because they didn't serve me anymore. That first night was really profound."

That first ceremony began a process of inner work that went much deeper on Gohar's relationship with himself. There were often dark aspects to his journeys, some more hellish than others. Moving through them and facing what he'd been hiding from enabled Gohar to progress his healing.

Each time he drank the medicine, there was a strong theme of self-care. It was time to look after his physical health. Reject the negative thoughts and constant self-criticism. Let go of past hurt and short-circuit the damaging mental programmes that obscured who he really was.

Gohar said: "In one ceremony ayahuasca clearly showed me how I was hurting my body. My body was crying, it was like a baby. I remember holding my leg in my hands, like cradling a baby. I was saying 'it's okay, I'm so sorry'. Feeling so much love for myself."

****

Wednesday 14th March, 2018, was a sunny day and Gohar returned to the farmland ayahuasca retreat. Forget alcohol, celebrations or partying…continuing on his inner journey was exactly how he wanted to spend his 21st birthday.

It was a daytime ceremony outside in nature, starting at 10.30am. Thirteen people had arrived, more than usual for the earlier ceremonies.

The group sat on mats in a cleared spot, with trees arching over above them, creating a cave-like covering. Gohar found a spot next to a tree and was relaxed as the sun shone on his face.

This time the medicine tasted really nasty, felt like drinking blood. The effects hit Gohar fast, the bright yellow field being covered with a green and blue tint within 10 minutes.

The familiar feelings of anxiety began so Gohar started focusing on his breathing. Gusts of wind were coming in and began carrying the anxiety away. The strange looking penguin/crocodile hybrid golden spirit from previous journeys appeared once again. It led him into a new dimension which looked like a grand palace courtyard.

Everything was made of copper and gold, there were hieroglyphics in the background, and Gohar saw himself relaxing in a hammock staring at a sky full of stars. A Chinese dragon came to him and it was like meeting an old friend.

Being with the dragon he was learning to connect with his inner child before the experience. The journey continued with Gohar being taken through beautiful fractal tunnels to his amazement. Mother Ayahuasca asked "what do you think of this?" before inviting him to go one better. He conjured up colourful scenes with a stream of shapes, taking part in a thrilling game of creativity...and trying to outdo Mother Ayahuasca.

Next stop? Gohar had visions of entering a church - and was greeted by his ancestors. A group of relatives who have died, all lined up to greet him with smiles on their faces.

"I got this really warm, strong feeling of them being really proud of me," said Gohar. "Proud of me for working on developing myself and they were really happy with where I am now in life.

"It was like they were there to build my self-confidence because that's something I've always struggled with. They didn't say anything to me but were all there to express their happiness and pride. The message I got is that I'm exactly where I need to be in life, I just need to be patient.

"All of these relatives are dead. It was like they were visiting me.

"I was teleported out of the church and saw visions of myself as a God-like being. All these different variations of myself in a positive light that made me feel super empowered. It made me more confident in who I am."

Gohar opened his eyes slightly as the sunshine covered his face. He felt a masculine energy from the sun's rays beating down on him.

One of the facilitators did some energy clearing work in his heart and throat. Gohar looked around and took in the beautiful surroundings, as the facilitator said to him: "You're in the most perfect spot ever."

Gohar lay back and looked at the branches above his head. They became like healing hands, pulling hurt and long-held negative emotions from his body, and then letting them go to be carried away with the wind.

Nature had become nurture, looking after Gohar. Freeing him from past pain. He cried, taking in the beauty of the outside world without the usual dark clouds hanging over him.

Closing his eyes again, Gohar got an important message from Mother Ayahuasca: that he needs to strive for balance in his life. He saw visions of a tightrope and keeping himself steady and upright. Going back to his old life and not caring for himself meant falling. Staying balanced meant looking after his body and mind, making positive choices for his own benefit, and allowing his creativity to grow.

Another ayahuasca drinker to his right had finished his experience. He looked over at Gohar, and said: "Happy birthday my friend."

****

Life was beginning at 21. Gradually removing mental and emotional blocks on his journeys with ayahuasca kickstarted a new health-focused journey in Gohar's daily life. He switched to an Ayurveda dietary plan and follows a plant-based diet. Gohar slimmed down from 340lbs to 218lbs in the five months that followed his first ayahuasca ceremony.

Tai-chi became a daily practice, along with doing positive affirmations in the mirror to build a healthier relationship with himself.

He said: "I'd like to say I've totally fixed that but I'm about 90% of the way there and I've been working with a therapist. Now I'm me - and I'm really happy to be me. I have a different perspective on all the failures and problems in life. They all arrived to help me grow.

"A couple of toxic people have left my life and new people more aligned with me and what I do have come into my life. I'm learning how to embrace life as a positive and negative balancing act.

"All these issues have been pinpointed and I'm now working on them. I didn't know I had such problems with health but properly looking after myself is my one priority now. I deeply feel for my body for what it's been through and I'm just really happy that my body hadn't given up on me, even though I had for a long time. These days there's lots of self-love and taking care of my body."

Working with the plant medicine and taking a closer look inside has resulted in a new type of freedom. Being able to let go of past resentments and understand the behaviours and projections of other people in his life.

"The most valuable thing I got was a deeper understanding of people," said Gohar. "For someone like me making art, being able to understand what people are going through means so much to me.

"Yes, the healing on its own has been amazing. But this ability to be able to relate to people and understand them now is the most beautiful thing ever.

"There's been so much forgiveness. Mostly not through ayahuasca, but through meditating. This whole process since December 2017 has made me much more open and forgiveness is such a huge thing."

Gohar is still a young man aged only 21 but his experiences with the medicine have fast-tracked his maturity…and removed some of the layers that had been hiding his true self. The acting is over. The fake guy has been fired. Gohar insists that is the real gift ayahuasca brings.

He said: "Everything that's not you is going to go away and you'll end up comfortable just being yourself. That's how it should be.

"Unfortunately, too often in society we have other people and the media trying to influence how you should be. We're flooded with other people's ideas about what we should be doing.

"What's more important is learning how to be yourself. That's what life is really about. Life is art and we are all individual artists.

"It's about learning how to be more comfortable creating your own painting."

CHAPTER 10

﹍

You have a choice

James Herlihy crumpled in pain as another headache completely overwhelmed him.

This time he couldn't shout on a nurse. He was at home in Cork, Ireland, and was supposed to be on the mend following a serious operation on his back.

Medics had accidentally sliced the spinal fluid sac in his back during the latest corrective surgery on his spine, but James and his family were assured he was going to be okay and he was allowed to go home.

Still the headaches came. James knew something wasn't right. That worrying feeling soon turned to outright panic after James stood up and felt the bandage on his lower back.

"It was soaked right through," said James. "As I turned to look at the wound spinal fluid sprayed out of my back!"

Medics told James to get to hospital immediately over the phone, but the journey was one hour long. His condition deteriorated as his dad drove him there.

By the time James reached the hospital entrance, he could barely walk and was on the verge of collapsing. The headaches flooded in so strong that James began vomiting.

He went under the knife again - his second surgery in a week - and James had to stay lying flat on his back for seven days for it to heal. The nightmare went from bad to worse as the headaches came back with a vengeance.

James experienced unbearable pain and ended up in a coma for three days, fighting for his life.

The severe trauma was too much to take. While James got better physically when he returned home, the emotional damage was deep and lasting. Extreme rage, sadness, anger, grief and fear grew within James. He blamed others for the situation he was in and the resentment was twinned with a deep depression.

From the moment he opened his eyes in the morning, James battled neurotic, repetitive thoughts. He couldn't shake the feeling of being victimised and let down by others. It was eating him up and he couldn't find a way out.

"I started looking for ayahuasca retreats," said James. "Something was drawing me towards it. I found Inner Mastery and I discovered there was a space available at the retreat they were holding the next week.

"I just knew this was for me. It was clear - right in my face - and I couldn't ignore it."

****

James travelled to the retreat but the fear began to kick in as he approached the building where the ayahuasca ceremonies would be held. Rosie, one of the retreat facilitators, gave him a hug on arrival. He was then warmly greeted by another facilitator, Arron, and the nerves subsided slightly.

James met the others who had signed up for three ceremonies, and he expected a relaxing introductory evening, possibly meditating. Then came the news that the first ceremony would be taking place in a matter of hours.

"Had I known this the way I was feeling earlier I might have turned the car around," said James.

Sitting on the floor on his mattress, James pretended he was fine. Inside, he was crippled with fear and anxiety, not just afraid of what was to come on his ayahuasca journey, but of simply being in a room with 20 strangers.

Finally getting his first taste of the medicine, James was surprised as it came on strong quickly. Seven years of repressed sadness, anger, fear, and torment flooded to the surface and overwhelmed the Irishman.

Plunged into a pit of negativity and darkness, James looked across the room and thought he saw another man die in front of eyes. In his mind the ceremony room had descended into chaos. Then James' mind switched to images of his family dying as the world began rotting around him.

James explained: "What really happened is that a lad across from me called Gerard had actually slipped and hit his face, but in my mind he'd dropped dead. The fear and paranoia was too much and I couldn't rationally understand anything that was going on in the room.

"Lots of people were crying and screaming. What was going on in my mind was a spiral of dark thoughts. I thought that Gerard had died and that we had destroyed the retreat. I believed the death of Gerard was causing a ripple across the planet. And it was all my fault.

"I then had to witness all my family dying and them being taken from me. I kept trying to escape the experience because it was so intense.

"I was then left alone at the end of time. I was holding a flower facing this massive entity that was the epitome of evil. I believed this had all really happened. This was reality in my consciousness. The whole world had died - because of me."

James was staring face to face with evil, having lost everything. His family were gone. Every other person on the planet had gone. The entity in his experience then asked James: "Who are you now?"

James explained: "Nothing of me was left. My entire existence had been taken from me and I was stripped down to my bare soul. But I still had this overwhelming feeling that I am good. I am here to do something good and bring it to the world.

"Those two words, 'I am', became my source of power."

Shown two sides of the same coin, James then had a choice to make. Darkness and evil - or beauty and joy.

And it was a choice. Just like blaming others, being negative, and hating his life before drinking ayahuasca was a choice too.

But now James knew that he was good in his soul. Despite all the dark drama and everything being taken from him, he knew he had a positive purpose in life. It had simply being overshadowed by the negative mental patterns sparked by his physical problems.

In his journey, evil was replaced with good as James came face to face with God.

"God came to me as a mirror reflection of myself," he said. "I was standing looking at myself and I knew it was a divine representation. Not that I was a God, but that God was part of me.

"This other version of me put his hand on my shoulder and said, 'you know it's all a big joke, yeah?' I was still in pieces after everything so at the time I didn't find it funny. But it was like hitting the reset button on a cosmic scale."

His first twisting ayahuasca journey had come to an end, leaving behind the death of his family, of the world population, being faced with evil, then God...and then the realisation that it was all one gigantic 'cosmic joke'.

One thing was no joke. James knew he was put here to do good and deliver it in a new way of living. His old self-destructive ways weren't working any more.

He knew the answer to the question, "who are you now?" They were simply "I Am".

The following morning after his terrifying introduction to the Amazonian plant medicine in his home country, James and the others did their best to try and prepare for what was next. The most powerful psychedelic journey of their lives awaited. This time the vehicle was toad venom.

****

James smoked the dried poison of Bufo Alvarius, also known as the psychedelic toad of Sonoran Desert. Bufo contains 5-MeO-DMT - very similar to the DMT found in ayahuasca - but with a few extra atoms.

"It was the most divine experience I've ever had outside of ayahuasca," said James. "It was far shorter - only about 20 minutes - but it was more powerful. I travelled at light speed straight into a divine realm. I then had a strange experience where I disappeared from existence. I wasn't scared; it was surprisingly beautiful.

"When I came back into the room everyone was paying attention to me and I could feel a cosmic love. It felt so powerful. I ran around the room and could see all this fractal love coming from people hitting me at once.

"There are no words to properly describe that experience, and that night my second ayahuasca ceremony was without doubt the most beautiful experience I've ever had."

Lying back with his eyes closed after drinking the ayahuasca, James was catapulted into the cosmos. Fractal ribbons, endless shapes and bright colours. All of it enveloped by love. James smiled widely. Even with his eyes shut, he could feel others in the room smiling too.

This time James was given the reins. He was in control of the direction of the journey. It was like his reward after such a horrifying first encounter with ayahuasca. Thinking positive thoughts, James saw bright, warm colours and pleasing images. When he briefly switched to negative thoughts, darkness made an appearance.

Pushing the negativity aside with ease, James became more confident in this switching game between two polarities. He had control so he continued riding the wave of love…until he was interrupted.

"I was smiling and laughing, but then this Devil-like character popped up in my consciousness," said James. "I could see the big red face and it came up right next to me.

"I was so good at skipping around these things now that I just skipped around the Devil and carried on. Then I felt bad for him, brought him back and hugged him.

"I told the Devil I loved him and thanked him for playing his part. As soon as I hugged him he burst into a huge flower of fractal ribbons, sparkly lights and dust.

"I learned that it's not all hard when you're dealing with your problems. It can be beautiful. You can find peace with your trauma when you begin having fun with it."

When it came to his third ceremony in three days, James' intention was just to go with whatever came up, and not try to control the situation. The medicine came on quickly again, making him feel really uncomfortable for the first 20 minutes, and he was struggling to pass through an initial barrier.

After surrendering to the struggle, James found himself in an unfamiliar place with some unfamiliar figures.

"I came across what I can only describe as entities," he said. "They had a human shape and features but were translucent with a very definite outline."

There were between eight and 12 of these figures grouped together like a gang, all communicating in a circle. They carried on chatting as James looked on quietly, trying to figure out where he was and what was going on.

One of the gang spotted James - and didn't seem happy about his arrival. The entity gazed over suspiciously and menacingly, and then alerted the rest of the group to the Irish outsider.

James said: "All of a sudden I'm faced with this gang of entities staring at me. One of them walked right up to my face aggressively and did some sort of war dance. He was right in my face and seemed really angry...but I didn't react out of fear. I didn't try to open my eyes or escape the experience.

"As soon as I did that he stepped back, smiled, and they all started clapping. They then welcomed me into the group with a hand gesture."

As James stepped forward the entities began touching his back and seemed to be working on the areas where he'd been suffering over the years. At this very moment the visions stopped and James was catapulted back into his own body.

As he lay on the floor, James' body began jolting like it did before when his serious back problems got worse. Only this time it was different...there was no pain.

He explained: "It felt like they were doing something spiritually. I definitely think they were helping to heal my back problems. The main message I got from the journey was that I need to be back in my body, rather than just in my head and focusing on the mental and emotional stuff. My body has been through a lot of trauma and I needed to be more present with it."

The whirlwind retreat had a draining but transformative effect on James. After some rest and gaining more complete strength, physically and emotionally, he was ready to do more work.

****

Travelling to Marbella for another two retreats, James participated in 10 ayahuasca ceremonies in just five weeks at the start of 2018 with Inner Mastery. He took centre stage in some more dark drama where his mind went into a frantic spin.

The old ways of his mind were being blitzed. Afterwards, James felt like someone had hit a reset button in his mind.

The dark, suicidal thoughts are gone. The circling feelings of anger, sadness, and resentment towards others and the traumas he experienced over several years have dissolved. The future's no longer bleak.

Ayahuasca has given James strength, Physically, emotionally, mentally and spiritually. The medicine has gifted him increased gratitude for his close-knit loving family and friends. It's boosted his confidence and reignited his passion for photography and videography.

The medicine has been the teacher. James is the student and is consciously implementing the lessons from his deep ayahuasca journeys into his everyday life. There were many teachings.

Some were the harshest lessons he'll ever encounter in his life. James has no doubt about the biggest one of all...

That he has a choice every day of his life.

James said: "The choice is between living in love and trying to be a good person - or living in fear and making terrible decisions.

"When you do something nice for someone that is a choice. When something bad happens to you it's up to you to choose how to respond. You have the ability to make the right choice."

Ayahuasca placed James on the road back to his true nature. While in Marbella, in ceremony number five, the medicine also catapulted him to a place he never expected.

James was taken back to an incident that occurred when he was a 13 year old boy. He'd had a strange experience he didn't understand while standing in front of the mirror, but had completely forgotten about it.

"Me, me, me, me, me, me, me…" the young James was saying to himself in the mirror. Gazing straight into his own eyes, the teenager repeated those words in a trance-like state.

The repetitive talking continued a few seconds more before James quickly snapped out of it. He panicked, and feared he was going 'crazy'. He'd no idea why he was speaking to himself, or what was going on in that unnerving situation.

Ayahuasca had taken James back to that mirror experience 25 years later to give him the answer …

Little James had just had a conversation with his Higher Self. The medicine showed him it was a moment of pure consciousness.

James said: "It was my Higher Self that had been speaking to me - and I realised it has been guiding me all along."

CHAPTER 11

~

Removing everything that's not you

"Can I drink ayahuasca with you guys?", Kent pleaded with Jesse for the second time.

The previous year Kent had asked his friend the same question, and was ignored. Jesse didn't think Kent was ready to be part of his closed ayahuasca circle. And he suspected Kent was only interested in tripping or getting high.

Yet here Kent was being more insistent, keen to explore and go deep within himself. But it wasn't as straightforward as just bringing Kent along. The community's regular ceremonies were top secret, as ayahuasca is classed as an illegal schedule 1 drug in America.

It was summer 2011 and the Amazonian plant medicine was still pretty much unheard of - never mind understood - where Kent lived in San Francisco. He knew little about its healing effects, but felt a strong pull towards drinking the medicine. He was determined to make it happen.

The special invitation finally came a few weeks later. The closed community would be together again when Francois was due to visit Northern California.

Francois was the curandero who brought the dark brown, murky medicine. The Frenchman had lived in Peru for many years and trained with the Shipibo tribe in working with ayahuasca. It had helped Francois beat a heroin addiction and he was then giving something back by bringing the plant medicine to people in the US.

An underground circuit was formed. Francois travelled from one community to another with the ayahuasca, bringing hope to Americans with medicine of a different kind. Assisting people to delve deep into their own psyche to heal themselves, rather than numbing their emotions and feeling stuck with prescribed drugs.

Kent wasn't on anti-depressants. To the outside world his life appeared to be going really well. Yet Kent wasn't happy and he had an inner knowing that "something wasn't right". It was time to go searching.

****

Kent headed for the countryside in Northern California after another stressful week in work. Climbing high on the corporate career ladder had been easy for a super-intelligent, hard-working guy like Kent.

Keeping the ladder steady while managing over 100 people - not quite so easy.

Jesse and Kent pulled up at their digs for the weekend after a long drive. A wooden building isolated in the countryside. The guys were joining Francois and his group for three ayahuasca ceremonies over the course of the weekend.

This makeshift retreat was a rough-finished studio space that had only the basics. An electrical cable that ran through the walls to a handful of power outlets and a light from the ceiling. A few four-paned glass windows. Just enough room for a maximum of 20 people to have their own space against a wall.

The mood was reverent. Kent sat on the floor feeling very nervous and anxious, not knowing what to expect. He'd intentionally avoided doing research and just wanted to let the experience unfold without any outside influences.

Francois sat facing the group of 15 people who had come to drink the medicine. He had dark hair, tanned skin, was aged in his forties. After serving ayahuasca to everyone, Francois sang Icaros from both the Peruvian Shipibo and Native American traditions.

In between his chants, coyotes howled outside in the distance. They always joined in the singing during his ceremonies.

The medicine began working through Kent, shifting energies and dragging out stuck emotions. There were few visuals but he quickly discovered this was far more than a psychedelic experience. Ayahuasca went much deeper.

In a matter of seconds Kent's mind was infused with a vastness of knowledge far beyond what his intellect had accumulated in 31 years. It was as if his brain had just been plugged into the Universe's USB port. His first time drinking ayahuasca, yet strangely the experience didn't seem new to him.

When called for his Icaro, Kent whispered to Francois: "This feels exceedingly familiar." Francois nodded knowingly, while Kent thought to himself, 'it feels like someone has cracked an egg of ancient wisdom on my brain.'

As he lay back and was pulled back into the experience, white letters were ingrained in Kent's head. They read: "Surrendering is the ultimate act of courage."

He knew that ayahuasca was trying to get him to relax. Kent was scared to let the medicine in. Scared to let other people in and get close. The message was that it takes more courage to let go, relax and be vulnerable than it does to step out and fight.

An important lesson for ceremony one and something he would continue to struggle with in future. But surrendering was what would get him through some of the darker experiences in many ceremonies that followed over the next seven years.

It was also clear to him that he needed to follow his passion of world travel - or wake up as old man one day regretting what he never did in life.

Kent returned to his corporate job on the Monday morning knowing life was never going to be the same. How could it? Life wasn't what he thought it was. Drinking ayahuasca was like first day in first grade. So much to learn - yet also so much to unlearn.

Kent's life pre-ayahuasca in one word…busy. Busy working long hours as vice-president of sales at a solar installation company. Busy progressing his developing career, busy making money. Always on the go, always running away from something.

With women he would rather play the field and not get too involved. It brought less stress, less risk. Through ayahuasca he began to figure out why.

Kent said: "It was a struggle of learning how to be intimate with other people and being vulnerable. I wore a really big shell and wasn't letting anyone in. At the point of drinking medicine for the first time I was freshly out of a relationship and simply didn't want to be in one.

"I was shown in future ayahuasca ceremonies and in working with other plant medicines that I had many emotional blockages connected to my parents and ancestry. This was affecting my behaviour and close relationships with other people."

After that first weekend, Kent hatched a plan to escape his hectic life. The pressures of work had been building every week. The suit just didn't seem to suit him so well anymore. His job inflated his bank balance and ego, but it was deflating his dreams of travelling across the globe.

It was time to leave everything he'd worked for behind and see more of the world. He knew he'd regret it otherwise…messages in subsequent ayahuasca ceremonies kept telling him so.

****

Within eight months of his first ceremonies, Kent had figured out an exit strategy and was on a plane. He knew Peru and the Amazon were part of his travel plans. The closed community Kent had been drinking the medicine with pointed him towards an ayahuasca centre in Iquitos.

Perfect choice - it's where he met Ana. Within minutes of arriving at the centre, he came across the Portuguese woman volunteering at the retreat, and was taken aback thinking, "who is this woman?" Within two weeks he was bitten and was keen to see Ana again, conjuring up an excuse to visit her when she returned to Portugal.

Kent had a loose plan to travel to Europe after South America, but Portugal hadn't been on his radar. It turned out Portugal would become his new home.

Clarity on his future came after a week-long plant medicine detox with Portuguese Curanderos, Geraldine and Abdel, of the Onanya Shipibo retreat. It brought new insights and a time for reflection. Kent looked at where he was and compared it to how he was living his life two years previously.

Left behind was the busy, stressful, workaholic lifestyle In America. Left behind was the hunger for success, desire for approval, and sporadically dating different women.

During his travels, Kent had slowed down. His focus switched from the external to the internal. Life was flowing, no more choppy waters.

The more Kent worked on the heavy issues internally, the lighter life became on the outside. Ayahuasca and other plant medicines brought past wounds to the surface that he was completely unaware of. They also revealed how he had inherited emotional blockages that had been passed down through generations of his family.

Kent's focus was directed towards his relationships with his parents, with himself, and how all the baggage he was holding onto weighed down on his close relationships with partners in life.

Kent said: "What I've learned is that there are some really heavy issues that come from my ancestry that have had to be cleaned. I don't have a complete understanding of what those things are - but some of it has to do with slave trading days.

"In processing those energies I realised I didn't have a relationship with anger and that was creating physical liver pain for me. As I developed a relationship with anger and accepted it's not something to be ignored, that led me to a maturation process.

"This in turn led me to having a better relationship with my father. It was fear of his anger that caused me to choose to repress mine as a child. Just healing that was so important, but the process took more than a year to clean.

"From then on, there was a focus on becoming a man through rites of passage. A realisation came that for boys to become men it takes other men…and I had been trying to find that through women."

One particular ceremony brought up a painful memory that had long been buried in his subconscious mind. One that had a strong impact on his ability to trust people and feel safe enough to open up and be vulnerable.

Kent had flashbacks of being molested by a babysitter when he was just three years old. It took more than three decades, and finding plant medicines, to process that traumatic memory and finally start healing.

A year and a half after first meeting in Peru, Kent and Ana became romantically involved. The plants and the inner work brought them closer…but it wasn't all love hearts and rainbows for the pair.

Kent was more than 10 years older. He wasn't a Portuguese resident - or allowed to work there. The chances of them settling down in America looked close to impossible. Even after getting engaged there were disagreements about what type of wedding they would have.

Rows were regular. The uncertainty about the future was a cloud hanging over them…and it seemed like they had a special knack of triggering each other's emotions. Tensions were up and down, and Kent and Ana came close to splitting up on more than a few occasions.

Yet each time they returned to the plant medicines they got through it. Each time they gained a new understanding of their own issues that were blocking their happiness in the relationship. They took responsibility for working on themselves - and their relationship always worked out for the better.

Kent said: "We go through our childhood as extremely sensitive creatures. All of us are going to be traumatised one way or another. As parents we try to limit that as much as we can. Those traumas are going to determine who we are attracted to and form a partnership with.

"It's my belief that we are attracted to who they are because they can trigger things in us that ultimately help bring those old traumas out. This gives us an opportunity to heal by feeling and discharging emotions that are stuck in the body.

"By constantly triggering each other, and being such hard-headed people, we force the other one to deal with their shit. It's been the best relationship and worst relationship we've ever had. It's those extremes that have created such a beautiful bond between us."

The couple continued working with Geraldine and Abdel at the Onanya Shipibo retreat and immersed themselves in 'dietas', working with several plant medicines. Geraldine and Abdel originally learned the dieta process from their Shipibo training, but adopted the structure from Takiwasi centre in Peru.

Takiwasi also specialises in treating drug addicts with the plant medicines and has an 80% success rate for those that complete the nine month rehab programme.

The Takawasi-style dieta involves isolation in nature for 8-10 days, eating a very restricted diet, and consuming specific plant medicines that heal particular issues in your life. These include the Amazonian tobacco mapacho, known as the father plant that provides guidance and a masculine energy, and other plants such as bobinzana, which supports emotional growth and helps to ground people.

Kent and Anna parted company, went into the woods near their retreat, and lived in small wooden huts for the duration of the dieta. On the first and last days of the dieta, they'd also drink ayahuasca - the mother plant - and it worked synergistically with the other plants to create an expanded shift in consciousness.

Each set of ayahuasca ceremonies was like a chapter in a book, the next part of Kent's soul story. Each dieta was like an entire sub-section in his book.

The chapters were all in perfect sequence. Kent couldn't have moved onto the next one in his life - and have it make any sense - if he didn't fully experience the previous chapter.

Kent said: "It's very interesting this work. There's no religion to it. The best category it falls into is animism. What I find fascinating by it is that almost everyone who works with the medicine comes to a similar view of the world. All done through multiple individual experiences to get there.

"I find it amazing how the plants get people to that particular way of seeing things. In our culture, we generally look at things very mechanically. Having to acquire a skill and then bolt it onto you. Acquire another technique and then bolt that onto your character. Needing to acquire the ability to speak or perform in a certain way.

"All these different things that we're working with the intellectual mind to acquire. Versus work with the medicine that's all about subtraction. It's the removal of everything that's not you…so that what's left is the essential, shining you. That process of subtraction is a lightening of your load; it really can't help but make you more content and more satisfied.

"For me, there used to be this 'moment' that I was searching for several years. Thinking, 'there's gonna be this big breakthrough'. I don't think there's an ending to that process. I think it just continues indefinitely.

"I see how this work continues to make my life better and better. There's no end goal in mind - it's just so beautiful to become more and more of who you actually are."

****

Seven years on from that first ceremony back in California, Kent struggles to remember the guy he once was. These days he's much more content within himself. Being intimate and vulnerable has become much easier. Earning an income has become a breeze. Relationships with people are much better now that he doesn't desire approval from others. His serious side is gone and he can laugh at himself.

Portugal is his home and there's a tremendous satisfaction in simple living. Kent's a successful online investor and it's paying for a comfortable life. The more he focuses on his inner feelings and self-development, the more the material things in life fall into place.

In 2017, Ana was considering a move to Amsterdam to study. Meanwhile, Kent was looking to settle down and was ready to become a father. With many arguments in the past, they both knew it was make or break time for the relationship. Which way would they turn?

Towards another plant medicine dieta. Towards Abdel and Geraldine who would guide them throughout the process once again. The plants would give them direction for the future.

By the time they returned home 10 days later Ana had made her mind up.

"I'm now ready to be a mother," she told Kent.

It was time to become parents - but not quite so fast. The dieta rules meant that sex was banned for 30 days. Immediately after their month-long wait…Ana got pregnant.

Kent said: "It was one of those synchronicities where you say to yourself, 'this is obviously the right time', and I think we had done enough work on ourselves that we were ready for it."

The couple knew they would never have made it that far if it wasn't for Abdel and Geraldine. So at Kent and Ana's wedding ceremony in Portugal in December 2017, Abdel and Geraldine were their godparents.

And in May 2018, Kent and Anna welcomed their baby daughter Naia May Calisto Halliburton into the world.

CHAPTER 12

⌒

Forgiving those who hurt me...and forgiving myself

"I really feel that you should pay this bill," the psychologist said abruptly over the phone.

She wasn't asking, she was demanding. Across the table from the psychologist sat Bernardine. Her eyes were puffy and her cheeks were still wet from the tears shed over the previous hour.

What was Bernardine's abuser thinking on the other end of the phone? How angry was he at being confronted by this psychologist he didn't even know. Would he even admit to sexually abusing Bernardine all those years ago when she was a child?

Bernardine asked herself all those questions as she tried to figure out how he was reacting to this unexpected phone call. There was no way she would have confronted him. Not on the phone, definitely not in person.

That's why her psychologist had taken the lead and called him herself. The health professional also knew there was no way Bernardine could pay for the counselling she desperately needed. It could run into thousands. Bernardine was aged 19, with a poor paying job, and with barely any savings.

Bernardine sat in silence watching as the psychologist started scribbling with her pen, while pressing the phone against her ear with the other hand. Bernardine could hear her abuser responding on the other end of the line, but couldn't make out the words.

"That's fine," said the psychologist. "I'll put her on the phone."

She handed the phone to Bernardine, who grabbed it nervously. She paused for a second before putting it to her ear.

"Hello," she said to him quietly. It was the first time they'd spoken in years.

"Don't ever contact me again," he replied before hanging up.

The psychologist smiled at Bernardine. He'd given her his credit card details and agreed to foot the bill. It would pay for the first in a series of sessions where the young woman would try to work through her childhood traumas. Try to understand why he abused her sexually for so long. Try to heal.

Being honest with herself, she didn't think counselling would make a difference. How could talking with a stranger undo nearly a decade of abuse as a child? More had happened before that too.

Bernardine had flashbacks of being abused by another man as a toddler. Her parents working or not at home, and the babysitter's partner touching her. Then another flashback of a sexual incident at friend's house when she was in primary school and her dad taking her to hospital afterwards.

So much torment for a young girl. Overcome with confusion, suspicion, fear, and distrust, Bernardine became a different person. Her heart, once open as an innocent child, was shut off to prevent further hurt. As a teenager, the mental pain and stifled emotions began to wear her down.

Feeling down, isolated, unbalanced. She should have been enjoying life like her friends were but anger was boiling up inside. Outbursts of shouting and being nasty to people were happening frequently - even though it wasn't in her nature.

The anger was always directed at older men. Usually for no reason at all. She either didn't like them, got irritated by them, or thought they were up to no good.

****

Bernardine and her older brother were brought up in South Africa. Her parents split when she was five years old and her mum later remarried. The children spent a lot of time with their grandparents while their mum worked.

Sometimes an alcoholic woman would babysit them, and her partner would sexually abuse Bernardine. The memories were hazy as she was only three or four years old. Bernardine was still certain that it happened more than once.

The memories of sexual abuse that followed with another man were clearer. They spanned eight or nine years, only stopping when she was aged 14. The distrust and anger towards older men were deeply ingrained - even after the series of counselling sessions her attacker paid for.

Bernardine's nightmare continued as a woman. A pattern emerged where she somehow fell into relationships with older men who abused her physically, mentally and emotionally.

First, the Englishman who ran a company supplying cheap foreign workers to factories and farms. He was in his early 50s, Bernardine in her 20s. What started off as simply a boss and worker relationship slowly developed. He bought her horses, gifts, and gradually won her affections.

The generous nice guy she'd fallen for became someone else whenever alcohol was involved. Which was often. He'd fly into drunken rages and fire horrible insults at her.

Bernardine wasn't allowed to go out at weekends. Wasn't allowed to spend time with friends either - so she lost most of them. Bernardine's one friend that remained invited her on a trip to Egypt - somewhere she'd always wanted to visit.

"While I was on holiday he was calling constantly and my friend eventually took the phone from me and switched it off," said Bernardine. "I knew then that I had to get out of the relationship.

"The first night I got back home he tried to strangle me. He was going to Scotland the next day on business and that's when I left and moved to the next city with some of the company workers from Lithuania."

A young woman in her 20s shackled to an abusive man in his 50s for two years. What was she thinking? Freedom had arrived - at last. Time to make up for it all partying with her Lithuanian pals.

There was plenty vodka, plenty party drugs, and they were all so friendly. One guy more friendly than the others. He seemed nice, only a few years older than Bernardine, and much more fun than the brute she left behind.

The new relationship moved so quickly. The physical abuse came quickly too. Within the first month Bernardine had a black eye. She had escaped one abuser in 2007 - and walked straight into the arms of another.

She said: "We moved to Scotland and then Bristol in England. During that time he would be verbally and physically abusive, smashing things up where we lived.

"It was frightening. There was a time when he grabbed a knife and threatened to kill my dog. I woke up one morning and the house had been smashed up. The door was open and my dog was missing. I looked everywhere for him that day. About 6pm someone came to my door with the dog. The man said my dog was frightened and had been hiding in his garage all day."

Friends asked Bernardine why she never left her cruel boyfriend. She didn't have an answer. It finally came one night when she took shelter in a women's refuge. A poster on the wall said "you love the person they are 90% of the time".

She was always looking for safety, affection, and a loving partner. She got it 90% of the time - and that's why she grinded out the relationship for four years until 2011.

Bernardine said: "I didn't properly realise at the time that there was a pattern with men and me. When we moved to Ireland I tried to get him help and we both went to see a counsellor. He stormed out of the first session and I ran after him.

"The counsellor told me to leave him but that he wanted me to come back on my own. Only by working with this counsellor did I realise that all of this was related to what happened to me as a child."

The relationship finally ended in 2011. Bernardine said goodbye to another scary, manipulative abuser. Sealed with a restraining order. A few years later she began dating a Hungarian man she worked with.

This guy was younger - and restored her faith in men. Temporarily. The first couple of years went reasonably well but he became emotionally abusive. Even worse, they both ended up hooked on heroin.

****

Living with her new boyfriend in Ireland, Bernardine started off smoking a 20 euros bag of heroin with him each day. Within months, Bernardine alone was spending 150 euros per day on the killer drug.

Somehow she maintained her job working with animals. Somehow her body was surviving such abuse day after day. But her world really began to fall apart when she lost her mum, dad, and several other people close to her in 2013.

Life was a mess. Saddled with huge guilt about not being there for her mum. Another relationship turning out like the rest. Another man treating Bernardine badly…only this time she was hurting herself even more with heroin. It continued for years and Bernardine wasted a large compensation payout she received for a workplace accident when she was on drugs.

Scrolling through Facebook one night in late 2017, Bernardine began reading about kambo - something she'd watched a documentary on a few years earlier. The frog poison that detoxes and reboots the whole body. She instantly decided she was having some of that!

Arriving at the Inner Mastery retreat the following month, Bernardine signed up for kambo, ayahuasca and bufo that weekend. She was all in.

"Fortunately I had 20 grand saved in a separate account from when I worked in England for thee years," she said. "My mum had always told me to spend my savings wisely on something important, such as property. Spending some of my money on this retreat felt right and I think my mum would have been happy I did. I wouldn't have been able to heal otherwise."

Before leaving the house Bernardine smoked more heroin. She expected a long weekend and worried how she'd cope without the drugs. Would she be desperate for heroin like on most other days? Would she end up sick and have to leave early? Her body was already sick - she had nothing to lose.

The prospect of detoxing her body and wiping away years of drug abuse was the main driver for attending the retreat. At the back of Bernardine's mind was also the sexual and domestic abuse that plagued her. She was desperate to finally let it all go…but not quite so enthusiastic about the prospect of reliving those memories.

Bernardine lay with her eyes closed, hearing noises all around her. Vomiting in the far corner of the room. A few groans to her left. Rosie, one of the facilitators, whispering to someone. Movement everywhere outside, but nothing shifting inside.

An hour must have passed already and still nothing, she thought. Bernardine opened her eyes and the darkened room looked the same. No bright colours, no blurry vision, no change.

She sat up, lay back down, focused on her thoughts. Yet everything remained the same. Still stuck in the same room, opening and closing her eyes every few minutes, one long repetitive cycle. The ayahuasca wasn't working. "Nothing is changing," Bernardine said to Rosie.

The facilitator said: "Ayahuasca shows you what's been going on in your life." Those words made no sense to Bernardine. The medicine had shown her nothing. All she got was one long, uncomfortable night of opening and closing her eyes, and feeling let down.

An interesting insight flowed into Bernardine's mind the next day. She realised that nothing was changing in her life either. That she was stuck in a loop of negativity. Years of drug taking day after day. One abusive relationship after another. Stuck in a rut.

It all made sense. Bernardine realised what it all meant - but she was disappointed she never got to work through some of her childhood trauma. At least smaller chunks that she could handle in her first ceremony.

None of what Bernardine desired had occurred, yet a huge shift had taken place that she hadn't quite grasped until the following day…

The insatiable heroin hunger had disappeared. The absence of her daily drug was not followed by severe sickness. The frantic mind always trying to figure out where the next heroin hit would be found was unusually calm.

Bernardine said: "At first I felt that I didn't have as many breakthroughs as everyone else. That's the problem with people having expectations in ayahuasca ceremonies. You can't choose. What she thinks you need right now in your life, that's what's going to be dealt with.

"When I was driving home after the retreat I just felt on top of the world. I realised that I did have breakthroughs - lots of them. Looking back now, I might have had more than everyone else.

"I just knew the heroin addiction was gone. I just didn't feel the need for it anymore. Even when I was driving home I couldn't wait to get a shower, read a book, and watch a movie. Whereas before I simply couldn't wait to get back and score a bag (of heroin).

"I knew after that first retreat that it was gone and I'd never go back to it again. I also found a new place to stay and moved away from my ex-partner."

Two weeks later Bernardine was drinking the medicine again. Before flying out to Marbella for the retreat, she did work with an energy healer and reiki master. All in the hope of releasing blocked energy and being more open to healing from ayahuasca. She drank with the intention of having no expectations and that whatever is meant to be will be.

In ceremony one, Mother Ayahuasca told Bernadine that her heart chakra was now unblocked and that meditation and breathwork would now be beneficial for her. She was also handed a huge list of people she needed to forgive.

Top of that list was herself.

****

Less than two months after her first drink of ayahuasca, Bernardine joined The Inner Mastery community once again. Bernardine prepared to look within and do the work.

The effects of the medicine were immediate, stirring up a mixture of emotions. Anger the main player. The man who abused her for many years in childhood took centre stage in her mind. The anger and tension intensifying each time she saw his face, or another hurtful memory resurfaced.

"I was trying to find a way to be able to forgive him, "she said. "But I didn't know anything about what happened in his past - what may have caused him to abuse me. So I struggled for what seemed like ages. I couldn't find a reason to forgive, but I eventually did simply because I knew I had to let it go.

"For the first time in an ayahuasca ceremony I was crying. I cried so hard for two hours because there was also sadness about my mum dying too, and not being with her when she died."

The next day at her group integration session the tears kept flowing. Bernardine spoke openly from the heart the words she wished she could have said to her mum before she died. Sorry that she hadn't been there for her more often. Sorry that she'd died alone. And a thank you - because her mum always stayed strong for everyone else, despite having her own problems to deal with.

In the following ceremony Mother Ayahuasca arrived inviting Bernardine to come with her. Bernardine held back, unwilling to follow. Like a scared child unsure of a stranger. Then the word "trust" flashed into her awareness.

That single word represented what Bernardine had lost in life. What was missing from her intimate relationships, and what was needed to be able to find stability and happiness.

The journey unfolded by reminding her of people who had broken her trust. The list of men who had treated her so badly. Ayahuasca showed her grudges she held onto firmly, but that couldn't really be justified any longer.

Yes she'd suffered at the hands of men who had abused her, but not all men treat women like that.

"These men began flashing up in my awareness and I knew I had to look for ways to forgive them," said Bernardine. "With my Lithuanian ex-boyfriend I remembered that his dad had hanged himself when he was two years old. He also came home from school when he was aged 10 to find his mum was dead.

"Obviously this caused his anger and I understood this was why he was lashing out at me. I forgave him and let it all go.

"With the older guy in England I found it more difficult because he was so manipulative, but eventually I remembered that his wife had died from cancer years beforehand. I interpreted his hurt from this death may have been why he treated me so badly. Realising this allowed me to forgive him too."

Forgiveness was also found for her last boyfriend. Bernardine reasoned that he was acting so badly and trying to control her because he was scared of losing her and being alone. On her final day of the retreat Bernardine worked with other plant medicines used for clearing chakras and restoring balance.

Sensations of a small ball being stuck in her stomach were followed by vague memories of her earliest sexual abuse trauma. Sitting at the forefront of her conscious mind, it couldn't be hidden away or avoided any longer.

Healing this wound was more complicated than the others because Bernardine couldn't remember the man. She knew nothing about him as she was only three or four years old when it happened.

Rather than find a reason to forgive this dark character that had always cast a shadow over her life, Bernardine acknowledged and accepted what happened. She sat with the feelings and surrendered to them. Later that night the feeling of the ball in her stomach was gone.

Decades worth of trauma dropped and discarded in just three days. Feelings of guilt and sadness over her mum's death finally released. The next steps on Bernardine's path have been working on her relationship with herself.

Building up her confidence and self-esteem. Developing herself free of drugs, overwhelming negativity, and away from people who did not respect her. The ayahuasca community she's now part of has delivered a whole new bunch of positive people in her life.

She said: "Along with forgiving other people, I forgave myself. I am proud of myself for everything I've been through. After my last retreat I decided that I would never let anyone treat me badly again…that I could stand up for myself.

"Before, I was very self-conscious, paranoid, sceptical, untrusting. I felt a weight on my shoulders and in my heart. I thought that I was happy but it wasn't true happiness.

"Now I just feel so light, content and at peace. Bring on anything. I feel like I can do anything now, whereas before I never had the confidence. I'm excited about the future...for the first time since leaving South Africa nearly 20 years ago."

Bernardine is looking to build a new life in Spain and feels a calling to help other people who have suffered sexual or domestic abuse, as well as drug addiction. Her heart is set on learning more about plant medicine healing and joining the Inner Mastery team that helped transform her life.

"Where I lived in Ireland heroin addiction is everywhere," said Bernardine. "Suicides happen every week. We must let people know there are other options for them. That's what I plan to do. Even if I can just help one or two people, that would be a good thing.

"Counsellors have said to me that I've been through so much for one lifetime. I've overcome it - and I obviously needed all of that so that I could help other people. I feel as if this was all meant to happen to me in order for me to find a different way out of it, and be able to help other people.

"Working with ayahuasca helped me release anger, and sadness, and allowed me to forgive the people who hurt me. To let it all go. I still believe, after doing all these retreats, that never in five lifetimes of therapy would you get anywhere close to healing as you do with these retreats.

"In a matter of months, I feel I've dealt with most of my shit. I'm happy to not even think about it anymore, it's all in the past.

"Thank you Mother Ayahuasca, Kambo and Bufo Alvarius, and of course thank you to Inner Mastery and the amazing facilitators. I hope and trust that my story might be an inspiration to others out there who feel trapped and close to giving up. There is hope and more importantly...this is the cure."

CHAPTER 13

~

Bringing the medicine closer to others

As Joeri Oomen climbed into the long boat, he immediately felt the tension from the group of strangers sitting around him.

As the boat began gliding through the brown, murky waters in the heart of the Amazonian jungle, Joeri knew it was going to be a long ride.

The young Dutchman was already tired from travelling more than 6,000 miles to Peru. The eight others from all over the globe looked equally drained and never made much eye contact. All were seeking help and heading for the Ayahuasca Foundation retreat in Iquitos.

The mood felt heavy. A few smiles and saying "hi" did not hide what was really going on. Everyone was in the midst of their own inner struggle. Too focused on the medicine that was to come in the rainforest to be concerned with small talk.

Joeri said: "Although everyone was friendly enough to one another, you could see that every one of them had something going on inside. Some sadness or problems…you could really feel it."

Depression, feelings of worthlessness, and emptiness weighed down on the boat that day. As each person stepped off and trudged into the Peruvian retreat, some of them questioned why they were even there. Their ego trying to convince them that a sunshine beach holiday would have been a better way to spend their money.

Three weeks later, Joeri was sitting outside on the last day of the retreat. He smiled as he heard the constant laughter at the table where everybody had gathered.

Giggling, loud voices, and occasional hugging. This group of men and women had only known each other for a few weeks…but had become like brothers and sisters.

Joeri would normally be sitting among them. Not this time. He was just observing everything at a distance. Enjoying a little bit of alone time on his last day in the jungle.

The trees were greener. The skies brighter. When he shut his eyes he could hear the birds chirping that bit louder.

It seemed like the group of visitors were being given a special send-off. Like nature was smiling at them for all their hard work with ayahuasca.

Joeri sat back in the sunshine and reflected on how so much could change in such a short amount of time.

When the group climbed back onto the same boat to return everything had clearly transformed. They all smiled deeply. Looked radiant. Conversation flowed and everyone glowed.

Every individual leaving on the boat was unrecognisable to the person who had arrived. All thanks to a series of ayahuasca ceremonies at the Peruvian retreat that guided them to places within themselves that they couldn't reach before - or even knew existed.

"This was the same people in the same boat, but you could feel that everyone was so much lighter," said Joeri. "All smiling like before, but truly lighter. You could feel the difference, which was really nice."

It was April 2016 and Joeri was a 27-year-old man in Peru looking for answers. Those profound transformations answered one of his biggest questions…about whether or not to continue with his personal mission. It was like a thumbs-up from the Universe to launch 'Ayamundo' and help other people access the medicine too.

****

Five years earlier, the young Dutchman felt completely lost. Still struggling with the death of his father when he was 18. Studying industrial design in Eindhoven but not completely convinced it was the right career for him. Confused and uncertain about the future, and trying to find his purpose in life.

Ayahuasca came on his path - and wouldn't leave. Joeri read about the medicine and was instantly attracted to it. Put out of mind, and then it would randomly reappear in his life a few days later. Popping up on the internet unexpectedly, or on the pages of a book.

It wasn't long before Joeri was booked in for his first ceremony with The Sacred Voyage retreat, one of the first ayahuasca centres to be set up in the Netherlands.

Joeri sat down on the mattress, crossed his legs, and shut his eyes. Dave was only a few feet away. Who better to share your first ayahuasca experience with than your best friend?

The men slipped into their own seemingly separate journeys as the medicine washed over them. The initial feelings of nausea didn't last long. Joeri's tired, burnt-out body was taken over by an unfamiliar sense of peacefulness and calm.

Life was still, there was no more hurry. In fact, it felt like life was about to begin...

Joeri was back in the womb - the womb of the Universe. Before this life or after this life? Joeri wasn't sure, but he was excited about the prospect of birth. Of being born from this surreal yet wonderful place of stillness and safety.

Whatever life he was about to be born into, a strong feeling came that he should never have to stress or feel worried. Before drinking ayahuasca, his tank was close to empty, and his mind was always busy with confusion and uncertainty about what to do with his life.

This journey was showing Joeri that it was time to take things easy. His life didn't have to be difficult. It didn't have to be stressful. It was possible to enjoy life more - and hang onto the sense of peace he found in the pre-natal dimension he'd just been immersed in.

Joeri looked over at Dave smiling. He wanted to wander straight over to his mattress and tell him all about this unreal experience. He could barely hold it in. But Dave had not quite landed back yet. He looked groggy and was still getting his bearings, as if he'd just wakened from a deep cosmic dream.

After each minute that passed Joeri hoped that Dave would sit up and come over. After an hour Joeri had had enough...he couldn't wait any longer. He stepped across the room quietly and slowly knelt down on Dave's mat beside him, making sure he didn't disturb others in the group.

Joeri asked his friend how he was feeling, before quickly adding: "I had this unbelievable experience that's hard to explain. It's like I was a baby in the womb again. Like I was waiting to be born."

Dave smiled, and Joeri went on: "But I was in the womb of the Universe. I felt so relaxed and happy."

"So did I!" said Dave, as he sat up properly in astonishment. "I had a vision of myself just before birth and feeling really at peace. I can't believe you experienced this too."

Having been friends for years, Joeri and Dave had already shared countless good memories. Many of them forgotten. But that night in Drenthe on September 7th, 2014, was etched into their minds forever.

Joeri said: "I remember the excitement very well. Dave confirming what I saw in my vision made the whole idea of a place where souls wait to be born again a lot more real to me.

"After a couple of months, I read the book 'Your Soul's Plan' by Robert Schwartz. His description of the place in between lives was very similar to what I experienced. It was remarkable."

One year later, Joeri had fallen back into old patterns. Working on projects that didn't satisfy him. The stress mounting. Straying from the path he was supposed to be walking. It all built up and pushed him in the direction of ayahuasca once again.

Joeri's second ceremony with The Sacred Voyage came, and the medicine showed him the impact living inauthentically was having on his life.

Walking along the wrong path in his career was draining Joeri of energy. The more he would stray away from the type of creative activities that fulfilled him, the more tense life became. Like a spring with tension pressing down on it.

It was an important insight. One he couldn't ignore - or his health would be faced with the consequences. From that moment on Joeri chose to make decisions based on gut feelings, rather than rational and fear-based decisions conjured up by his conflicting mind.

Those first couple of journeys in his homeland were invaluable. They gifted Joeri understanding, enthusiasm and allowed him to work through some stuck emotions that were preventing him from living his life fully. He also realised that there was much work still to be done.

He said: "I knew it was the beginning of a long process, but it gave me hope to deal with what was going on in my life and to continue working towards something. It was pleasing to know that whenever I would have troubles there was some tool - the ayahuasca - that I could fall back on that could help me.

"Slowly I started thinking about how I could use this experience to help other people. To do that in combination with the main thing I did well so far, and that was building websites. I slowly started building the Ayamundo website, but I still wasn't sure about putting it online.

"This was because ayahuasca still had a stigma around it. I wasn't sure how my family would react or what other people would think. So when I went to Peru in April 2016 I wanted to find out if this was something I really wanted to carry on with.

"I knew by the end of the retreat when I saw how all those people had changed. The group were sitting round a table in the communal space on the last day and I saw everyone smiling and laughing. That's when I knew the importance of bringing people together and allowing them these experiences.

"I could play a small part by pointing people in the right direction. That's when I knew this was the right thing to do."

****

Joeri quickly resumed his online work when he returned to the Netherlands and launched www.ayamundo.com soon afterwards. The main aim was to create an online service where people could find and book into a safe ayahausca centre that was right for them.

It became an online directory where people could properly check out a wide range of retreats across Europe and South America, and then make proper arrangements before travelling to the other side of the world.

Joeri appreciated that many people are really struggling in life at the time they seek out retreats. Helping people find the right retreat and removing any barriers to them accessing the medicine is what Ayamundo is all about.

Ayamundo lists dozens of retreats in more than 20 countries in South America and Europe. Ceremony participants can leave reviews on Ayamundo.com afterwards, sharing their true first hand experience of their chosen centre.

People considering drinking ayahuasca can even email those who have left reviews directly via the website. This allows website visitors to ask for more information and reassures them that the reviews are genuine.

Joeri said: "For me it was quite difficult to find good retreats. There were some websites but there weren't a lot of options to choose from. Also, when I went to Peru I had to make a down payment and bring a couple of thousand dollars with me. For some people this might be a problem.

"Ayamundo was also about making the trip less of a big step without barriers. It's already a big decision and you want to make it easier for people to eventually go."

The Ayamundo ambition is to make booking retreats via the website as easy as AirBnB. Clear terms on what you get at each retreat in advance, what you pay, and how the refund terms work. Between 2016 and 2018 the website numbers went from 0 to 4,500 visitors per month.

It continues to grow, with centres encouraging people to leave reviews at Ayamundo. With the number of ayahuasca retreats on the rise, more centre leaders are contacting Joeri to be listed on Ayamundo.

He said: "I get requests from retreats all the time. I contact them by email and also try to reach these people through Skype to find out a bit more about them and their retreats. It's really hard to judge whether a retreat is good or not. There's so many different centres and they work in different ways.

"In the Netherlands they have more connections with the Western world, whereas in Peru they are more traditional. They have different belief systems and it seems strange in the context of the Western world.

"It's hard to judge a centre, but that's why I want to leave it up to people who have visited and let them leave their honest reviews. In some cases, if I believe a centre is not legitimate, then I won't list them. A big part of the whole process is good communication between the centre and the participant. That is what we call a good centre."

Through his 'Ayamundo On Tour' video series, which can be viewed on YouTube, Joeri and the Ayamundo team visited nine centres in the jungles of Peru around Iquitos and three retreats in the Netherlands. The next planned visits are the cities of Cusco and Pucallpa in eastern Peru.

Joeri said: "Some centres are really traditional, whereas others have more Western elements to them. Some centres believe that there should be as few activities as possible, while others provide people with the opportunity to visit villages, search for alligators etc.

"I found that some centres have groups of 20+ participants, where retreats with different days have overlap, so you can be meeting different people every other three days. On the other hand, some centres have one group that stays together for three weeks. Some have various types of yoga, others have more adventurous activities.

"Often there is not a lot of guidance for people that start at their centres. I think there should be more information available to them about safety protocols and what to keep in a medical kit. Fortunately, a group of centres are founding the 'Ayahuasca Safety Association'.

"They aim to provide this information without restricting the centres in their practices, while also performing checks to see if all the member centres comply with the association's guidelines."

Since his first two ceremonies in his homeland in 2011 and 2012, Joeri has had another nine ceremonies in Peru. To him, the difference is like listening to live music and a CD. "When you are in the jungle the nature surrounding you is pretty dense and the sounds are also pretty dense," he said.

"You hear all these animals and of course the shaman singing his icaros. It's really a different experience. It wasn't necessarily better than in the Netherlands, just different.

"When I first drank ayahuasca it felt like I discovered a tool that could help me when I needed it. Before that, I wondered what I should do with my life and what would really make it worth living. Through ayahuasca I got hope that there's always something that can help you in life. From no hope to hope.

"Many people put ayahuasca on a pedestal, like it's the only solution. I think it can help a lot of people but it's not for everyone. You have to be open to it. I think that the more desperate you get the more open you will be to trying ayahuasca.

"There can be a healthy combination of treatments for people and it doesn't mean ayahuasca has to be a part of it. I do think that the way in which people view ayahuasca and the way it is illegal in many countries means that people are denied a good tool that definitely could help them.

"That's the thing I don't agree with. It doesn't necessarily mean that everyone should drink ayahuasca, but everyone should have the opportunity to drink if they wish."

That trip to Peru in April 2016 gave Joeri a sense of direction and provided the energy, desire and drive to complete his Ayamundo website. The ayahuasca experience also gave him the opportunity to let go of the past.

Joeri explained: "Around eight months beforehand, I started to feel a knot in my chest and I knew it was to do with emotions that I hadn't let out. In Peru, it really became clear to me that it was sadness, happiness and many other emotions. I wasn't able to tell what was what…and that's why it was stuck.

"Each ceremony in Peru was like a knot unravelling. An emotion would become the topic for each ceremony and they were all processed one by one. Everything I am now was there already…I just discovered more of those parts.

"On my most recent trip to Peru I didn't drink ayahausca because I simply didn't need it. I'm not sure when I will drink again. For now, my ayahuasca path is to help others find it."

CHAPTER 14

～

Lifting the veil

Veronika Poola was thousands of miles away from Spain…with no idea of where her travels would take her next.

The round tent's white sheets circled behind her. The dome sitting snuggly above, illuminated by the sun's rays. Veronika stood out front in the fields in England enjoying summer. Enjoying nature. Enjoying being back in the UK with Lorenzo.

It was the summer of 2005 and Veronika and her partner Lorenzo were at their first raw food festival. Loving the vibe and the people. Especially loving the food. Following a raw diet was a big factor in Veronika recovering her physical health after her nervous breakdown just two years earlier.

One guy in particular seemed really impressed with the yurt they had brought with them across Europe. Jim was a tall Englishman. He was friendly, smiling and, after shortly introducing himself, Veronika quickly felt comfortable chatting to this stranger.

"Where are you both going next?" asked Jim.

"We're not sure yet," Veronika replied. "But we're not ready to go back to Spain just yet."

"Well…." said Jim. "There's a 10 day summer camp coming up in Cornwall next month where we drink ayahuasca. Why don't you both join us at it? If you brought along your yurt, I'm sure the organisers would find it useful for the camp…and you'd probably get in for free."

Extending their holiday sounded appealing. Free entry for 10 days? Really appealing. But what exactly did 'summer camp' mean?

"Have you heard of the Santo Daime Church?" asked Jim.

Veronika and Lorenzo looked at each other and shook their heads. "No, never," replied Lorenzo.

"Or ayahuasca?" said Jim.

Veronika was intrigued because she'd heard of ayahuasca when she was a teenager. But there was a problem this time. Jim had also began talking about 'Christ' and 'the church'. Too many religious terms were slipping into the conversation. Veronika began to feel resistance.

An atheist for as long as she could remember, she wasn't interested in God, church, prayer, or anything that went with it. Plus, none of that really tied in with her idea of a summer camp. It certainly didn't fit in with what she expected ayahuasca would be like.

Yet somehow Jim's offer seemed like too good an opportunity to miss. They didn't have to travel. The camp was right there. They could get in for free.

Veronika and Lorenzo discussed the offer a few times during the food festival until finally agreeing that they would go. The enormity of it was completely hidden - at least until the end of the 10 day camp.

At the Santo Daime church, Veronika slipped into the row of people at the back of the room. Everyone was friendly and welcoming. Still, she felt completely out of place.

Dozens of people were dressed in uniform with matching shirts and ties. Veronika, Lorenzo and the rest of the group were wearing white clothes as requested.

Four rows of people were lined up standing in a square shape all facing towards the centre of the room. Jim was down the front near the leaders. In front of them was a table with a Christian cross on top of it.

The singing began. Songs to Jesus, just like at church, but more upbeat. The energy in the room was shifting, but Veronika felt awkward. The whole situation was a bit surreal.

Three or four songs in and everything changed. That first cup of ayahuasca that Veronika had drunk 30 minutes earlier began to kick in. A sense of panic crept in. Paranoia quickly took over and Veronika became hyper-aware of her surroundings - and her heightened feelings.

"Oh my God, what have I done?" Veronika said to herself. "This is what my parents warned me about religious cults. Now they've given me this substance. They've brainwashed me."

Surrounded by 80-100 strangers. Feeling nauseous, vulnerable, scared. The tension in the room was at breaking point. Veronika wanted to escape, but felt trapped. The ayahuasca worked through her body, the singing seemingly giving it directions.

As the group moved through their collection of seemingly never-ending songs, Veronika simultaneously felt herself moving through the period of panic. Like she had just gone through a thick patch of and could begin to see clearly again.

The mental fog continued to clear to a whole new level of clarity. The intense feelings fell away and were replaced by calm and joy. Veronika realised that her view of life had always been hazy. That something was always blocking its beauty. Reality had just come sharply into focus.

"I felt as if my whole life I'd been walking about with a veil in front of my eyes," said Veronika. "It was as if ayahuasca lifted that veil - and I saw reality for what it was for the first time.

"The whole night was really strong but by the end of the night everything had changed. I'd also made peace with the whole Christianity thing, the uniforms, and the whole structure of Santo Daime because I had a very beautiful experience in the end. I thought, 'if this is a cult then fine - this is one I want to be part of'."

****

Before that first intense experience drinking ayahuasca Veronika had been smoking tobacco. Not constantly, but it was an addiction she couldn't shake off. After that first ceremony she woke up the next morning and threw the tobacco away. She couldn't stand it any longer, instinctively knowing her body would reject it.

It was completely unexpected. As was the comment made by the Englishman leading proceedings. "You have a very strong path with Santo Daime," he told Veronika. She didn't know what he meant, but he was one of two ceremony leaders.

By ceremony three Veronika was called to stand next to them both. Right down the front with the most experienced drinkers. It felt as if she had intentionally been placed there where she would learn most quickly about ayahuasca and the Santo Daime.

The medicine came on strong. Much stronger than before. The effects so overwhelming that Veronika couldn't move her body. A force began to pull her away. Where? She didn't know - but she was going and had no choice about it. Pulled into another dimension that was strangely familiar.

It felt like she was dying. A tunnel of light ahead was drawing her in.

As she edged slowly towards the light, Veronika became aware of a counter force. Several people were pulling her back and saying, "you've got a mission here, you can't go right now."

She tuned into those voices and was overcome by a wave of intense emotion. This carried her back into her body. Back to reality...but starting afresh. The powerful experience had been like a death and rebirth. Everything felt new and light.

Veronika and Lorenzo continued drinking ayahuasca for the rest of the 10 day camp. On several occasions she stood in the front row with the leaders again. Ten days of the deepest inner work summed up in one word - intense.

But both Lorenzo and Veronika emerged from it as completely different people. Both felt reborn, but something else completely unexpected materialised for Veronika.

"Up until that point I considered myself an atheist," she said. "During that first retreat I knew that I no longer was. I came out of it and felt like, somehow, I had physically touched God. It was like tangible proof to the existence of God that I left with.

"This, for me, was a very big revelation. I was someone who did not think of any experience beyond this lifetime or reality."

The Brazilian man, Maurilio, who had brought the ayahuasca to the UK, had also spoken with Lorenzo earlier in the retreat, saying: "Why don't you organise a Santo Daime retreat in Spain in a couple of weeks? We can bring the ayahuasca, drink together, and hold a few ceremonies."

The way everything was unfolding was surreal to them, but it also felt natural. As if it was all part of the script. Veronika, Lorenzo, the Santo Daime church leaders, even Adrian who they met at the food festival…they were all just playing their parts.

By the time the 10 day retreat was over Veronika had no doubt she and Lorenzo had been placed on this path. Their new life was about to start.

****

Just a few years earlier, Veronika's life was a misery. She'd been living in Montreal, Canada, until aged 25. Studying criminology and psychology at university, the young woman was always unhappy but hoped she would land a good job and be able to live a normal, comfortable life.

But life was anything but comfortable. Depressed since she was a teenager, Veronika struggled daily to maintain balance and set off travelling before moving to Scotland in her mid-twenties.

As she got older this was getting increasingly more difficult. Veronika felt irritable, anxious and had no idea why. Dabbling in recreational drugs, smoking, and drinking regularly made life even heavier.

A sickness that would not shift led Veronika to the hospital. There were too many symptoms she couldn't explain. She just wanted to be properly checked out and given medication to clear it.

But Veronika wasn't prepared for what the doctor told her.

"I'm afraid you've got a sexually transmitted disease," he said.

"What?" she replied quickly. "That's impossible…"

Veronika paused to try to make sense of the diagnosis. She couldn't. The results must be wrong, she thought. Veronika did not have a boyfriend. And besides…

Suddenly, her mind's process of recall and reasoning were replaced by a horrifying memory. Then another frightening scene, and another. She sat dazed in the hospital room as painful flashbacks occupied every inch of her mind.

Veronika had been raped several times. The experiences were so painful that her body had completely shut down and the trauma was immediately consigned to the smallest box in a corner of her subconscious mind.

Veronika had been abused in her late teens, and again in her early 20s, yet she couldn't remember one second of it. Completely repressed, out of sight where it supposedly couldn't hurt her anymore.

But it was always hurting her. Always lurking in her subconscious mind where she couldn't actually see it. In a matter of minutes in the hospital consultation room, the lid had been blown off that small box and the contents were clear to see.

There was no denying what had happened and there was no other place to bury the trauma again.

From that day on, Veronika's life spiralled out of control. Post-traumatic stress was added to the depression in her doctor's notes. The medications piled up. As did the side effects. At one stage her suffering and cocktail of pills resulted in a stage of psychosis.

Veronika felt helpless and regular sessions with her psychiatrist gave little relief, or hope of a way out. She was drinking every night to the point of passing out - and then loading up on caffeine just to get through the next day. A nervous breakdown followed.

It was going to take something dramatic for Veronika's circumstances to change. Something radical. Her change in lifestyle was exactly that.

Veronika moved to Spain in 2003 and began living outside in nature. Connecting with the outdoors, plants, and wildlife away from the city chaos.

It gave her mind some much-needed respite. Switching to a raw foods diet, and fasting regularly, gave her body the support it needed to physically heal.

Slowly, Veronika tried to rebuild her life. Her relationship with Lorenzo gave her hope for the future. As did their unique home in the Sierra Nevada in southern Spain. Located between mountains above the nearest town and living outside in yurts, the outdoors brought a sense of calm and she loved the simple life they had there.

A population of just 6,000 people in the town, with 60 different nationalities registered at the city hall. A very eclectic bunch of people into many different things. Also very open to various different spiritual paths. She'd lived in Canada, Scotland, and America…but Spain had become home.

However, the couple's love for raw food and travelling inspired a trip back to the UK two years later. So they packed up their yurt into their van…and headed for Cornwall on a summer adventure that would change their lives forever.

When the couple returned to Spain after the ayahuasca summer camp, they listened to their intuition. They acted upon the advice that they had a "strong path" with the Santo Daime. Everything came together magically. The right connections, the right people, the assistance they needed.

Within a few weeks they were holding Santo Daime ceremonies on their land. Church members from Brazil supported them in getting set up. They also travelled to Brazil, and back and forth to England again, as their work with ayahuasca deepened.

Just as in Santo Daime tradition, Lorenzo and Veronika held ayahuasca ceremonies every fortnight. Using the Amazonian brew as a sacrament. That practice began in 2005 and they have been working as facilitators ever since, serving the medicine hundreds of times.

In 2015, they began holding three day ayahuasca healings at their 'Amoraleza' retreat. In 2018 they introduced a nine day retreat, which consisted of four ayahuasca ceremonies combined with yoga, a day of silence and extended integration.

The Amoraleza retreats are unlike most others in Europe. Ceremonies are held outside in nature in a white-coloured dome. A fire burns in the middle and participants sit around in a circle before receiving the medicine.

The sounds of singing, drums, guitar and other instruments fill the dome throughout the night as each ceremony progresses. Songs from the Santo Daime, icaros, Spanish ayahuasca songs, and sometimes even mantras. At times there are periods of silence to settle the energy or go deeper into the healing process.

Decades earlier, the land was used for other spiritual ceremonies involving sweat lodges, the plant medicine peyote and also ayahuasca. Drinkers arriving from all over the world often comment on feeling a strong connection with nature during and after their ayahuasca experiences there.

Accommodation at Amoraleza is a basic yurt or wooden cabin. There's very limited electricity and no wifi across the four hectares of land. Participants are asked to not spend much time on their phones. The main aim is to connect with nature and each other. Food served is vegan and mostly raw, organic produce.

They began ayahuasca ceremonies in Spain in 2005, led by Maurilio. After several initial sessions, he left Veronika and Lorenzo with the medicine and encouraged them to continue working with ayahuasca. By this point Veronika's life had already been completely transformed and by helping countless other people it changed her whole experience of life.

"Ayahuasca has made me a lot more compassionate, a lot more patient, and a lot more understanding of the human experience," she said. "It's also given me a lot of focus. The first time we drank ayahuasca I was then asked if we could hold space for ceremonies here."

The healings that have taken place at Amoraleza through ayahuasca have mainly been of a psychological nature. One powerful life transformation in 2017 stands out in particular. The woman was aged in her 40s and was, for decades, carrying a pain that Veronika could relate to.

Veronika said: "The woman had been raped, either as a child or as a teenager, and she'd been carrying this with her for her whole life. She hadn't actually put it on her form before coming here, but before the ceremony she said, 'I think I need to tell you this because I've had a lot of trauma around it'.

"She had an amazing transformation in the ceremony and came out of it as a different person. We also had another woman who had suicide attempts in the past, depression, and post-traumatic stress.

"That only came out after the first ceremony, which was also very strong. We held space for that - and she also left as a different person and has had a complete life change."

Each Amoraleza retreat involves up to 20 people and includes deep integration work in between ceremonies and before leaving. Participants form a sharing circle on the final day and pass a feather round while opening up about their journeys, lessons, and how they're feeling at that moment.

The most beautiful part of the work for Veronika? Seeing the way people blossom.

"Seeing the way people open up is special," she said. "There's a certain openness and vibration on the land here. People often come from cities and have a lot of things they need to process. It's amazing to see the people becoming real again. People come here wearing a mask. It's just a persona of trying to be.

"They drink the medicine, have the experience, and then I see the real person. At their core, not what they're trying to project."

No matter how powerful the experience is, or how changed the person may appear, Veronika and Lorenzo always have a strong message for ayahuasca drinkers: the work has just begun.

Veronika said: "A lot of people these days look for a quick fix. Like the whole pharmaceutical industry - you take a pill and the problem is supposed to go away. With ayahuasca, she'll show you what you need to do - but really you have to put in the effort afterwards.

"The ceremony is the easy part. I compare it to giving birth. Once you're raising your baby and child afterwards, that's a lot of work.

"It's important to have other tools. Yoga, meditation? Or it could be psychotherapy. Ayahuasca is one thing but if you don't have other tools to put everything you've learned into practice then you lose the magic and the gifts."

Letting go has facilitated a smoother journey for Veronika over the years. Letting go of expectations. Of desires. Simply trusting that Mother Ayahuasca will give her what she needs most, not necessarily what she wants.

This is another important message she and Lorenzo pass on to people who drink ayahuasca at Amoraleza. People can be disappointed if they have specific wants and try to control the outcome.

"The main teaching for me is to surrender," said Veronika. "Mother Ayahuasca has taken me to deeper and deeper levels of surrendering. Inside the ceremony experience so much happens and you cannot do anything to change it.

"It's really about trying to apply that to my everyday life too. Each time I drink she'll show me where I'm still stuck from not surrendering enough.

"Working with ayahuasca has given me a strong connection with the spiritual realm too, and faith that once this life is over there's something afterwards. It's really helped overcome the fear of death. That's been a great gift."

In her third ayahuasca ceremony Veronika detailed going through a near death experience. The indigenous people of the Amazon embrace this type of journey and consider it a prerequisite for spiritual awakening. Hence why ayahuasca is referred to as 'The Vine of the Soul' or 'The Vine of the Dead'.

Whether it's this terrifying prospect, or being faced with the darkest aspects of our characters, Veronika has simple yet invaluable advice for people to overcome difficult times in their ayahuasca journeys.

She said: "Rather than pain, negativity and anything the mind can grasp onto, I focus on the breath during ceremonies. It's the mind that creates the suffering. If we just breathe then it can really easily disappear.

"If you're in ceremony and in a moment that's really difficult because you're afraid, really anxious, or are in a lot of physical pain, you can't actually do anything in that moment except surrender.

"In the really difficult times the mind starts to think, 'why did I do this?' 'Is this normal?' It goes into a loop - and the only way to break that loop is to focus on the breath.

"If you're truly focusing on the breath - as it's taught in meditation and many different spiritual practices - the mind can't go to its thoughts, and eventually it releases.

"In my third ceremony the experience was so strong and so physically painful that the only thing I could do was breathe. Forget what the mind is worrying about, stressing about, and just focus on the inhale and exhale. That's what got me through and can get us through anything."

Now aged 41, more than two decades have passed since she was raped. Finding ayahuasca meant that Veronika could also find a way to remember that deep trauma and release it. It meant that her long-standing depression and post-traumatic stress disorder could finally dissolve.

It helped Veronika create a happy fulfilled life with Lorenzo and their four children in Spain, where they share the medicine with hundreds of other people from all over the world each year.

"When I began on this path I didn't really understand what was going on," said Veronika. "In those first 10 days of discovering ayahuasca in Cornwall everything was just happening like magic. There was a realisation that, yes, magic is real. There is something guiding us. There are signs.

"It gave me faith that there was a higher power that was holding the puppet strings. That I'm not in control of what is going on. There's a higher power that's deciding.

"I have free will - but I don't have control over any situation. If I can relax into that and just accept everything that comes, then that's how I can find peace."

CHAPTER 15

~

Healing that can only be described as magic

April 29th, 2001 - the day destiny played roulette with Felipe Saldarriaga.

The 11-year-old woke up that Sunday with his friends. A bunch of boys had slept over at his friend's house in Medellin, Colombia. The lads were excited about riding on mini quad bikes later that day.

But Felipe didn't feel right. A painful headache from the second he woke up just wouldn't shift. When the boys began racing on their mini ATVs, Felipe got off after the first lap and fell to the floor.

It was unexpected; his legs just gave way. He quickly got back to his feet for another lap on the ATVs, but when he walked away afterwards he collapsed again. That second time he couldn't stand up.

An ambulance was called and paramedics rushed Felipe to hospital. Tests were carried out but the doctor was confused because nothing was showing up. Felipe's dad was called and he gave specific orders for his son to be sent to another hospital, despite medics wanting to keep Felipe under observation for 48 hours.

Felipe vomited in the ambulance and everything became hazy. He was becoming weaker by the minute. As he was being rushed inside the emergency room, Felipe saw his mum looking down on him and felt her touching his hand. Then everything faded to black.

Felipe woke up the next morning paralysed. No movement from head to toe, zero sensations in his body. For the first couple of days the 11-year-old boy was so overwhelmed by confusion to even begin worrying or getting upset at his horrifying situation.

His parents were at his bedside. Other relatives came to visit, while a series of nurses and doctors checked in on him regularly. Seemed like everyone who came to visit was extremely happy that he was alive. Felipe kept hearing the word "miracle" time after time. He just kept thinking, "what happened?"

A few days later, the doctors explained what had happened. Felipe had suffered a stroke. One that had clothed the main artery of the right hemisphere of his brain for over six hours. How it happened to such a young boy - and how Felipe survived - was a mystery to medics.

Felipe's family were told that three hours is the maximum time limit people can endure a stroke without irreparable brain damage. He'd gone six hours with no oxygen going to his brain, and emergency surgery was needed.

Doctors told Felipe's father: "There's a 95% chance your son will end up in a vegetative state. I'm afraid that if he dies, there's a 100% certainty we won't try to revive him."

Felipe's dad gave the green light for the procedure. He'd no option, his son was struggling to stay alive in front of their eyes.

"And if the worst happens?" the doctor asked. "Just let him go," his devastated father replied.

Years later, his father told him that in that moment speaking with the doctor he surrendered to the Universe, God, Pacha Mama or whatever higher power for the firsttime in his life. By letting go of his son's life and trusting that higher power, he found peace.

Felipe pulled through. Day by day, the boy started to get stronger. Despite the brain damage and little hope doctors gave him of a recovery, Felipe was out of bed and taking his first steps by day 28. Within three months he was able to walk again, although his movement was poor.

The doctors couldn't explain it. Neither could science. They simply called Felipe a "miracle". Because Felipe's case was so rare the United States government sponsored physical therapy and studies to try to figure out why the stroke occurred in such a young boy.

They did all types of blood work, scans, tests while Felipe tried to learn basic tasks such as tying his shoelaces again. It was just Felipe and his mother living in the US, his father having stayed at home with his sisters in Colombia. They had all been a really close family before the stroke and Felipe was feeling really lonely in a foreign country away from everyone he knew and loved.

Months later Felipe was sitting in Morristown Memorial Hospital in New Jersey with his mum. The test results were due back, they were both expecting to finally get some answers. The doctor examined the clinical history in disbelief before saying, "this medical history is wrong; it's impossible that this is real."

One by one, doctors came into the office for a second, third, fourth, fifth, sixth opinion until finally seven of them were taking part in a discussion on Felipe's medical history and the stroke. After two hours of deliberation one of the doctors, who happened to be Colombian, approached them and handed the history and test results back to Felipe's mum.

She asked if everything was okay, and he replied: "Everything is perfect ma'am. Medicine will never explain why the stroke happened or how Felipe survived and is standing next to you. It's a miracle; you enjoy your son."

That day Felipe told his mum he wanted to go back home to be with his family. He was confused, tired, and fed up of being called a "miracle". As his physical recovery stagnated in Colombia and Felipe couldn't live the same life he had before, he grew up despising that word.

If he was a "miracle" child then why couldn't he walk properly? Why couldn't he play football with his friends anymore? Why did he feel broken?

****

Felipe's world became a battle against negativity. His life was limited physically. For too long he wandered in a mind polluted by limiting beliefs. The contradiction of being a miracle and feeling miserable, while alienated from his own body, only created more guilt inside. Feeling obliged to smile bigger on the outside, but feeling emptier inside.

Felipe said: "Every doctor I'd ever spoken to told me how lucky I was, yet I couldn't do all the things that other kids could do. On one hand I was feeling like a victim, then on the other hand feeling terrible because I was supposed to be feeling really grateful about life.

"So you go through life smiling and pretending everything is okay, but you're also wishing things would be different for you. I went to bed every single night for 10 years wishing life would have been different. Why me? Why not someone else?"

Aged 21, Felipe moved to Argentina to study journalism and film production. He produced a film with an academy award producer, a dream come true. A city like Buenos Aires opened a lot of opportunities, meeting people from all types of cultures. Yet Felipe had never felt so empty and had some of his darkest moments there. Fortunately he had some good friends who helped him pull through.

Ten years on from the stroke, he was drinking too much alcohol and doing no exercise. His spirit was crushed by the reinforced belief that he wasn't enough - and that his body would never heal again. Every single night he went to bed dreaming of a different life, a different landscape in a different world. The "why me and not someone else" victim paradigm still running in his head.

Felipe felt that he never matched up in life. When he was 11 he had to be in a wheelchair. When he walked he had to walk more slowly. He couldn't run or play properly with his friends. Thoughts of feeling not good enough, not being worthy enough, repeated and normalised. Over time those thoughts were reinforced - and became Felipe's reality.

His constant projections had replaced his sense of self. He'd lost his identity. It would require a massive disruptor to give him a new perspective on life.

By the time Felipe came to ayahuasca in 2015 it was out of curiosity. There was no special calling, no synchronicities. Felipe paid close attention to the medicine through interest of internal investigation, but he certainly wasn't going to jump right in.

Taking note of the growing ayahuasca tourism industry in South America, Felipe was wary of the inauthentic. Cautious of people making money from ayahuasca, but not having the capacity or proper training to properly serve this sacred medicine. This led to a delay of many months until he found Don Luis Portilla.

Members of the Kogui tribe in north Colombia drank with Don Luis in the jungle. They are considered one of the wisest indigenous communities in Latin America. If Don Luis was good enough for them, he was definitely good enough for Felipe.

****

"Ayahuasca is the mirror of consciousness," said Don Luis. "It is a mirror for your soul, not your body."

Felipe listened intently as the shaman explained the work of ayahuasca in his culture. They were sitting outside Don Luis' home, a place in the mountains only 40 miles from where Felipe grew up in Medellin. The house looked like a big concrete barn surrounded by forest. A fire pit was the centrepiece of the large garden.

It was September 2015 and they both sat together as Felipe prepared for his first ayahuasca journey during the day. Felipe soon learned that his ceremony would not be like most of the others he'd read about. There were to be no songs, music, moving around, or other people round the fire. The ceremony was simply to be an exercise of Felipe and his soul in silence.

Don Luis was raised in an indigenous community with his plant medicine master, who told him: "The truth can only be found in your silence." If you go deep within, the answers will come.

Shortly after drinking his first cup of ayahuasca Felipe lay down. Twenty minutes later he was in the toilet completely feeling completely disarmed as the effects took over him. Felipe's mind flicked through thoughts of past experiences with mushrooms, LSD, and marijuana. He was frantically trying to find some sort of comparison to normalise what was happening - but it was impossible.

The ayahuasca was so strong that the purge came within the hour. "Why the fuck do people take this?" Felipe said to himself. He couldn't get his head round it, but within a few hours his view had completely changed. Felipe felt so light, so clear, like he was levitating. The end result made every bit of struggle worth it. The next day he had no hesitations in drinking ayahuasca again.

In the three months that followed, Felipe returned to Don Luis' home and drank ayahuasca 7 or 8 times. It was never like a retreat with a group of people at night time, rituals, or group sharing afterwards. Felipe always arrived during the day on his own, drank under the watchful eye of his shaman, and jumped on the rollercoaster taking him to deeper and deeper levels within himself.

Each time Felipe's intention was to let go of what was holding him back in life. He'd always ask for forgiveness for what he may have done to others. Then it was a case of slipping into the experience sitting in gratitude, with the mantra, "thank you father, thank you mother." Whenever Felipe felt overwhelmed, he'd return to the mantra, repeating it over and over.

The deeper the experience, the more Felipe was healed physically. During ceremonies his body would ripple and his arms and hands would move around erratically - without Felipe putting any thought or effort into it. Each ceremony brought improvement in his movement, posture and overall physical condition.

Almost three years on from his first ayahuasca journey, Felipe has drunk the medicine around 40 times. Always with Don Luis, and occasionally bringing a close friend along. Felipe's posture has improved significantly, not just with his shoulders but the rest of his body. He walks better, even talks better. Every drink brings a slight improvement in every area of his physiology.

"I've experienced super healing to a level of...the only way I can describe it is magic," said Felipe. "I'm still far away from regaining full control over my body but the improvement with ayahuasca is considerable compared to the other treatments I've had. It's helped me make the best progress in my physical health. For my emotional and mental health it's by far, far the best practice I've ever done."

Mentally, Felipe cleaned up his polluted mind and replaced it with a rock-solid perspective. Negative thought patterns were broken and instead he began to see points of view evolving - without being in the middle of them. Observing thoughts, creating feelings - but without identifying with them.

It was a practice, and gradually became a new way of being that liberated Felipe from the constant noise in his head.

He said: "For me, the mental and emotional healing that came with ayahuasca was getting to see all those thoughts and feelings unfolding - and reframing them in a different way. It's about reframing thoughts and events in your life so that they can better serve you.

"Like, what happened to me in childhood didn't happen because I'm a victim. It happened as an accident and turned out to be very valuable. All of this happened so I could be the person I am, and learn to relate to people the way I am. It happened so that I could learn that there are seven billion of us monkeys in the world and we're all doing the best we can.

"So have compassion for other people. Don't judge yourself so hard. Reframe things to serve you today."

The physical rehabilitation stunned not only Felipe, but also his family and friends. More of them began opening up about their own problems and struggles in life. Listening to their gut feeling about ayahuasca about whether it could be good for them.

Dozens of his friends from Colombia, Canada, Germany, Spain and beyond have since visited Don Luis with Felipe - and he insists that not one of them didn't have a positive, life-changing outcome.

Felipe said: "I had a friend who discovered that his biggest fear was to be alone. He had an experience of himself in a little boat in the middle of a storm, but then felt two hands holding him and comforting him. Then there's other people who have stronger physical experiences but don't go into the vision world.

"It's the most personal, subjective experience you can have as a human being. It's an experience that's going to make you rethink the relationship you have with yourself. Every one of these friends has had a positive experience, but I've met other people who go elsewhere and get sick.

"Especially when they go to the deep jungle in the Amazon. They think that A + B = ayahuasca. No, what you have is a nice tea made from chacruna and the vine. But from that point to turning it into a medicine, and for healing properties, I would only take it with a person like my shaman, with his experience."

Brought up as a Catholic, Felipe had a notion of God and religion. Then after surviving the stroke as a boy he was constantly bombarded with idea that he was a "miracle". There was always a degree of gratitude to be alive, but the resentment over his physical disability had prevented any relationship with spirituality.

That all changed after drinking ayahuasca.

Felipe explained: "For me, with ayahuasca, I don't believe in God…I have been with God. I am at one with God.

"You feel in touch with all of life and when you come into contact with that energy, the only result is compassion. The only result is patience. The only result is love. It helps you improve your day to day life.

"When I take ayahuasca it's like recharging a lighthouse. You fill yourself with so much love, so much compassion that you can go back to your daily life and be more productive and better serve your team, company, family. Reorganising my relationship with spirituality, in the end, is just changing the relationship with myself. It has definitely improved my life on a really high level."

The physical improvements have made life more fulfilling. Destructive mental programs have long been short-circuited. But the most valuable benefit from drinking ayahuasca for Felipe is the level of control he has over his mind, and his experience of life.

"The biggest thing for me is the ability to shift my path and observe my thoughts as they happen," he said. "If they're not helping me create the reality I want to experience, ayahuasca has given me the tools to hack the thought process - and pivot into thoughts that are better for the situation I'm in.

"You get better and better at it. And you always reframe with gratitude, compassion and love. That for me is by far the greatest thing. I can observe my thoughts without identifying with them and being charged with emotions…because those emotions can make us act irrationally.

"I don't block negative thoughts necessarily, but I observe them and can see where they're coming from. Thoughts that are rooted in my childhood are easy to spot, and now they don't have any control over me. It's the ability to observe them and inquire why they are happening - then stopping them the moment that introspection is done.

"Now I have power in my life. Now I can live every day with the certainty that the processing of life is in my control. That doesn't mean that shit will stop happening, because it won't. But when you have perspective of the bigger picture, and you have felt that you are a drop in the ocean, it empowers you in life."

CHAPTER 16

~

Be kind to yourself

I sat in the doctor's office in a daze as he was telling me some story about his brother also being unlucky in love.

I stared vacantly at his brown tweed suit jacket, hearing his posh English voice ramble on in the background, until one surprise word instantly woke me up…

"Wanderlust".

I'd never heard of it before. Why did he say that? What did it even mean? As I left the doctor's surgery and walked towards my car, I still had "wanderlust" stuck in my head. Weird.

In that visit to the doctor's surgery I was just glad to be somewhere else. Somewhere away from my family's drug addiction, alcohol addiction, and the heartbreak of yet another failed relationship. I was supposed to be the strong one in the family, the high achiever, the guy that's always got it together.

I'd tried so hard to fix the broken people round about me…but then I crumbled. Emotionally, mentally and physically. Aged 34, back living at home with my mum after a devastating break-up with the girl I love. I felt at the lowest point in my life.

Shortly after getting home from my doctor's appointment, I logged onto Instagram and the first thing I saw was a video of Dr Wayne Dyer talking about ayahuasca. "Try not to judge it, it's not about getting high," said the spiritual author. "It has nothing to do with that at all. It's a way of reaching your highest Self."

When my friend went abroad to take ayahuasca a couple of years ago I did judge him. I thought he was just getting high. But Wayne Dyer speaking so favourably about ayahuasca caught my attention. Then, on the same page on the same day, I noticed a quote about ayahuasca, this time from Dr Gabor Mate.

It read: "Ayahuasca is not a drug in the Western sense, something you take to get rid of something. Properly used, it opens up parts of yourself that you usually have no access to."

I immediately switched to Google and began searching like crazy for more information about ayahausca. 'Emotional healing', 'miracle medicine', 'feel reborn'…the internet descriptions of this jungle brew began to get me excited.

The more I read about ayahuasca, the more I felt pulled towards it. I started searching for locations and prices of ayahuasca retreats. Clicking in and out of websites frantically, feeling a sense of urgency.

I came across 'The Temple of the Way of Light' in Peru, which offers an intensive healing retreat mixed with ayahuasca and yoga. The yoga teacher's name? Marta WANDERLUST. I was hooked. I knew ayahuasca was for me. A trip to Peru was tricky due to flight times and costs, so I decided my first ayahuasca experience would be a bit closer to home.

Spain? Holland? Portugal? My friend Kat sent me a text the next day, and I told her I was going abroad in a week for a relaxing break away.

Kat replied: "Ok. Are you going to let anyone know where you're going? You know I worry." Kat then sent me a holiday offer link on the travel website kayak.co.uk, which included the headline: "A Cure For Your Wanderlust! 18 Destinations For Under £50."

Wanderlust – again! Things were getting strange and I felt like I was getting some sort of jumbled up message from somewhere. I just couldn't figure it out. The next day I booked up to join a retreat in Holland for two ayahuasca ceremonies on March 23rd and 24th, 2017.

It couldn't come quickly enough, felt like every cell in my body was thirsty for the mysterious Amazonian medicine.

With one week to go, all I could do was watch every video and read every article I could find online about ayahuasca. So I did…I was obsessed. One article titled 'My Journey With a Life Altering Drug: Ayahuasca' in Elle magazine caught my attention the next day.

American writer Arianne Cohen explained that she'd recently become more interested in ayahuasca. That she'd first discovered it when it appeared in the storylines of two movies.

She wrote: "It made cameos in Weeds and Wanderlust". The movie "Wanderlust", starring Jennifer Aniston, was released in 2012. I've still never seen it. Turns out there's a scene in the film where the actors drink ayahuasca!

They say that most people get 'the calling' to drink ayahuasca. That the medicine comes to you, rather than the other way round. I didn't know exactly how that was supposed to work out, but I figured the Universe was dropping me a pretty big hint.

****

I'd always loved playing cards, but I wasn't exactly playing poker in the Netherlands. We were all dressed in white, myself and my two facilitators, Jules and Delilah. The ayahuasca ceremony room in their countryside cottage was filled with ornaments, colourful paintings, candles, and had a real Amazonian tribal theme.

The deck of Wisdom Keeper Oracle Cards were spread out on the floor in front of me. Delilah and Jules were seated on small wine-coloured cushions, while I sat cross-legged facing them on my mattress on the floor. Two purple basins were on the rug behind me.

I picked out the "Enrichment" card. It read: "My gift to you: I come to bring you true enrichment, not mere enjoyment or entertainment. I want you to get the most out of your life, so that you can enhance the lives of others. But first you must learn to balance fun with seriousness. And you must wake up to all of the ways you distract yourself from who you are and how you truly feel.

"It's time to learn to discern from that which truly nourishes you, and that which saps your spirit. Notice where you are still a victim of your senses, of over-indulgence and self-deprivation.

"I care less about what you do than where you come from. Come from fear, and you'll likely do too much, too little, or at the wrong time. Come from love, and you won't need rules and protocols to guide you. Eventually your attention will turn inwards to gratitude, and your presence will enrich the world."

The lesson from that card I chose - along with my own personal intention - was to be the theme of my first ever journey with ayahuasca. To prepare for the ayahuasca journey, each of us snorted liquid mapacho, one nostril after another. The sensation from the liquid tobacco was like stinging nettles had been rammed up my nose. My brain felt warm and my nerves instantly calmed down.

I held the small ceramic cup of ayahuasca close to my chest, then closed my eyes as I put it to my lips and swallowed the bitter, earthy drink. I'd been sitting on my mattress for 10 minutes with my eyes still shut and then lay down.

As my lower back rested on the spot where my backside had been, it felt freakishly warm. The heat started spreading slowly all over my back, then gradually down into my legs. I could literally feel the medicine reach for every corner of my body.

I lay completely still with my eyes shut but it felt as if my body was moving in a wave-like motion from side to side. It took a few minutes before I realised I was moving like a slithering snake.

The music was getting louder. So were the gargling noises from my stomach. Then the strangest sensation on the inside of my calves and knees. Like lots of tiny needles moving under my skin.

My head started getting light and I began to see the geometrical shapes that so many others talk about. Lots of diamonds moving across my field of vision...green, purple, yellow. Swirling around slowly, bursting outwards and then coming back in closer to my vision.

The shapes turned into faces – half mythical features, half-medieval looking men with beards and piercing eyes. None of it really making much sense.

Shortly after drinking my second cup, the atmosphere swiftly changed. The visions halted, replaced by anxiousness and my body became more tense as I lay there in darkness. I suddenly felt like I was transported into a tribal ceremony in the jungle. Couldn't see a thing but it was clear that I was lying deep in the Amazon and I was at the centre of a tribal ceremony at night.

Tribal drums were being beaten slowly and loudly. "Gunnggggg............gunnggggg..........gunngggggg......" Louder and just a little faster with every beat. Then the hissing sound of maracas, and as the volume increased so did my anxiety and pressure in my chest. It kept building until I flew up from the floor and purged into the basin.

Jules rubbed my lower back and when I lay back on the mattress the drums had stopped. As if they'd only been leading up to this release. Then came a woman's voice. "Stand up and be counted...you are recognised in the spirit world," she said.

I fell in love with the idea that Mother Ayahuasca was speaking to me. Looking back, it was more likely vocals from the background music

Jules was playing. Either way it didn't matter, because I connected with those words.

They had a powerful meaning for me. I'd spent my entire life trying to impress everyone, from my mum and school teachers to friends, girlfriends and people I'd met for the first time.

I wanted to be recognised. I wanted to feel worthy. To feel good enough. My daily life was orchestrated around trying to fill that hole and earn my self-worth and respect. But it was always out of reach.

First I thought I could achieve my goal by being the most clever boy in the class at primary school. Then it was scoring for my school football team and winning trophies just like my uncle did nearly 40 years earlier.

My obsession with weight training began at age 16. Not because I wanted to be strong and healthy - but to feel attractive and match up to other guys to whom I felt physically inferior.

Always trying to over-achieve, earn more money, make people like me...needing to feel appreciated, recognised and wanted.

"Stand up and be counted...you are recognised in the spirit world." I then knew I had my place where it really matters when my brain stops working and heart stops beating.

Everything felt lighter after hearing those words and, as I sat up smiling, Delilah walked over and asked to hold my hands. I'd only met this Dutch facilitator for the first time a few hours earlier, but it felt comfortable and enjoyable. No awkwardness. We held hands for the next 15 minutes as I sat with my eyes shut.

I lay back on the bed to melt into the relaxing atmosphere and felt I'd been transported into a massive cathedral. I floated through the roofspace, past huge pillars, the colours all white and gold. A woman was singing classical music just for me. Felt like I was glowing. A message came to just let myself smile…that I don't smile enough in life.

Who knows how long it lasted? But I was sure it was the most beautiful experience of my life - and told Jules and Delilah so.

"Did you see your uncle?", Delilah asked me. "My uncle? No," I replied, a bit confused. "Your uncle was here. He said he's really proud of you."

I glanced over at the small pile of photographs I'd taken on the trip with me. At the top was the picture of my uncle Stevie. He'd died 13 years earlier.

****

Ceremony number two was due to begin in a few hours…and I had a horrible gut feeling that it wasn't going to go well. Jules, Delilah and I walked through the woods near their home together. The stroll was supposed to be relaxing and prepare me for my second ayahuasca journey, but I couldn't settle.

"I'm a bit worried about this ceremony," I said to them. I waited for their reassurance. For them to tell me that I was wrong, nothing to be scared of. Silence. "I know I just have to face what I have to face," I said next, trying to put on a brave front. Still I heard nothing back and we carried on walking in silence.

The ceremony began back at the cottage three hours later and with the three same steps. Picking a wisdom card for the theme of my journey, inhaling the stinging liquid mapacho, and then drinking the ayahausca brew.

I chose the "mindfulness" card, which read: "My gift to you: I am here to help you remember. And to release you from the prison of your emotional life. Even if you want to speed up enlightenment, you can't. So give yourself plenty of permission…to think, to feel, to desire, to react, to hide. Let nothing be forbidden.

"All I ask is that you be mindful of what you do. The first step in awakening is realising that you've been asleep. So do not try to change your patterns or passions. Just recognise them. 'Ah, there I go again.'

"Catch yourself forgetting your true nature. Learn to feel increasingly comfortable with discomfort. In time, you will naturally come to realise that something more wondrous than you can imagine is looking through your eyes, thinking through your mind and living through your actions."

This message never made much sense, but became clear in the months that followed back home. My intention for ceremony two: to be able to form lasting loving relationships – and to face whatever was blocking me from achieving that.

A couple of years earlier, I'd become aware that my parents splitting up when I was aged around four had messed me up. I had abandonment issues that killed every close relationship I had. Either I got too needy and basically throttled the relationship, or my girlfriend just couldn't fill my never-ending need for love and I began looking elsewhere.

I remember reading the book, 'Loving What Is' by Byron Katie where she explained that when we have emotional problems we first need to look at our relationship with our parents. My dad had been back in my life from the age of 16 and I thought everything was okay.

Driving home from work one night in September 2014, I realised I wasn't. I had flashbacks to when I was a toddler and him leaving on the train. I never saw him again and my mum later told me that I cried for my dad constantly for a month.

By the time I reached ayahuasca I was well aware this was a major emotional wound from my childhood. But I didn't want it to ruin my future and I knew I had to take a look deep inside to try and let go of the past and change the direction in my life.

I held the cup of ayahuasca close to my heart as I said my intention about forming loving relationships out loud. Within 10 minutes I felt nauseous and barely managed to keep the bitter brew down.

I fully expected harsh lessons from the medicine about how I'd treated past girlfriends badly. How I'd messed with their feelings or didn't respect them enough. Made to feel the same hurt I'd caused them.

It didn't happen. Instead I saw visions of my younger sister Stacey. Images of her as a cute kid with pleats in her hair and wearing her primary school uniform. Photographs of her that I'd forgotten even existed. She looked so innocent and happy – much happier as a child than as an adult.

Revisiting old memories, I walked through moments where we smiled together and were much closer as kids. Times when I thought better of her and didn't judge her. The comparison between then and recent years shown clearly to me. All I'd been seeing was her drug addiction, her chaotic lifestyle, and the hurt she'd caused our family.

I'd resented her for it, even though that's not who she really is. The reality is that's she's still a beautiful, innocent little girl needing love and attention just like us all. My head dropped down to my chest and I felt an overwhelming wave of guilt and shame.

I'm her brother. Flesh and blood. And I'd held all these negative feelings towards her because of her behaviour.

My intention was to find out why I couldn't make things work with any of my girlfriends. How could I have expected to have a proper, loving relationship with another girl when my relationship with my own sister was so badly broken?

The purge came and I prayed this was Mother Ayahuasca cleansing me of the guilt and shame. I wanted to be more compassionate towards my sister, it had just been so difficult. Delilah held my hand as my body trembled and tears came flooding out. I could feel my body loosen up more with every tear that fell.

I confessed to Delilah about the breakdown of my relationship with my sister. How things had changed since we were children. She said: "It's okay, it's not your fault. You were living unconsciously."

Cup number two was served...and the medicine kicked in quickly. "Be kind to myself". I didn't hear any voices say these words or even see them in my mind, this message had just filtered into my awareness. Next came "be gentle with myself."

Without my brain even trying to comprehend what this meant for me, I had an instant knowing. I woke up to the fact that I'd never properly cared for myself. It was so obvious - yet I'd been completely blind to it until that moment.

I didn't care for myself. In fact, my inner critic had been in complete charge of my mind for the previous 30 years. Criticising every second move. Judging what I did, whether it was good enough, whether I was worthy enough.

My pre-ayahuasca perception of myself: I'm a hard-working, ambitious guy that holds myself to high standards. I spend my life always setting new goals, expecting so much of myself, always trying to achieve.

My new perspective: that's all fake, a cover-up. The reality is that all of that activity was being driven by my deep feelings of inadequacy. My inner critic hiding in my sub-conscious mind continuously whispering insults and making judgements.

Self praise. Self love. Self acceptance...none of them were ever given a chance.

"Be kind to myself. Be kind to myself..." Those words repeated in my mind and I began saying them out loud. Nothing was more important than those words, everything else became insignificant.

I'd asked Mother Ayahuasca to learn how to have a lasting loving relationship. I realised that could never have been possible with anyone else when I'd always treated myself so badly and didn't love myself enough.

I clasped my hands against my heart and started rocking backwards and forwards whispering "be kind to myself, be kind to myself..." My voice was really soft and quiet, repeating those words over and over. Delilah came in behind me, leaned over my back and cuddled me. I felt her loving warmth and kept rocking slowly and saying the words to myself.

Suddenly I realised what I was doing…comforting myself. Being the parent to my inner child. I lay back on the mattress, held my hands against my heart and my breathing completely changed. Inhaling and exhaling in a peculiar, slightly faster rhythm with a squeaky noise at the end of every breath. It sounded like a baby.

Hands against my chest, lying back, strange breathing...cradling my inner child like a baby. Giving my inner child love like I always should have. Caring for myself – for the first time in my life.

Delilah asked if I wanted a third cup and I immediately said yes. I figured Mother Ayahusca was being gentle with me because I'd treated myself so badly for so long. That I'd got it wrong earlier worrying about how tough the ceremony would be. The theme of the journey was clearly all about caring for myself and looking after myself for a change.

"Some more of that please", I said to myself as I drank the third cup of ayahuasca.

****

I told Jules and Delilah about the importance of what I've just learned about myself. How I'd no idea I'd neglected myself for so long, how I couldn't see I was my own worst enemy.

They nodded, sat quietly and watched me closely as the third cup of ayahuasca flowed through my body.

I noticed the room had gotten really dark, apart from a few candles. And then...jolt! I felt a sharp movement in my body. A sense of panic rushed in afterwards. Ready to purge again – but this didn't feel familiar at all.

The mood in the room completely changed and there was no going back. I was scared. "What the fuck have I done? I shouldn't have drunk the third cup!", I screamed inside my head.

The vomit arrived from deep down in my stomach and it splurged out violently. "Be kind to myself, I need to be kind to myself," I was saying out loud in between each bout of sickness.

But the voice was more aggressive, like a parent or teacher telling me off harshly. Repeatedly slapping my palm hard against my chest as I said the words. My whole body felt like one huge balloon of negativity and it was ready to burst with this evil, disgusting stuff inside me.

I tried to stand up but couldn't. My legs like jelly, my head spinning, my vision blurry. Jules helped me to the toilet because I'd lost all control of my body. I sat on the toilet pan with the basin on my lap too as I purged from both ends all this evil, horrible, dark liquid. It seemed never ending.

There was a brief lull and suddenly I realised that I was talking to myself in a trance-like state. I'd been commentating on what was happening the whole time.

"Garbage out!", I shouted angrily. Garbage? An American word I never use, it's not even in my vocabulary. Where did that come from - and where did the voice come from? It sounded like a young boy who was really upset. Things were taking a deep, dark twist...and I began to doubt if there was any way back.

"I'm a good person. I need to be kind to myself." These angry words were coming out of my mouth – but this was not my script. "We're getting rid of allllll this garbage," I said firmly and loudly as I flushed the toilet. "We don't need it. It's gone forever...." I shouted as I stood up and pointed towards the toilet pan.

As I sat back down on the toilet it felt like I'd become a teacher delivering extremely harsh lessons to my inner child. The lessons....

"I must be kind to myself." Because I've been beating myself up for too long.

"I'm a good person." Despite what I've repeatedly been telling myself.

"It's time to get rid of all this 'garbage'." The criticism, self-judgement, and self-imposed fears I'd built up for decades.

My body was the garbage can and it was full to the brim with all negative self-talk and self-loathing. It was time to get rid of all that garbage, but to do that I needed to see and feel exactly what I'd been doing to myself.

Forced to re-experience all the hurt, pain and damage treating myself like this had caused. I felt myself getting sucked into a dark dimension where everything I'd left behind on earth was irrelevant. None of it mattered because this was what I needed to face – and there was no getting away from it.

The walls in the tiny bathroom started closing in on me. Thousands of tiny yellow squares on the wallpaper moving quickly towards me. My body was being twisted like a wet cloth being wrung out, and the voice kept repeating the same words from earlier. But I was speaking much faster and with panic in my voice, close to crying.

The energy in the entire house built up to palpable levels. Everything physically shaking, chaotic shouting noises in the distance. Jules opened the toilet door and I saw terror in his face when he looked at me. "I must be too far gone", I told myself. There's nothing he can do. I shouldn't have drunk the third cup. No way he could save me, I was on my own.

As Jules closed the door to the outside world, I sat cowering on the toilet pan, rocking back and forth like a scared little boy. Terrified. Clearly shown that treating myself so harshly and not having any self-worth was literally eating me up from the inside – killing myself. If I didn't stop I'd develop cancer or some other horrible disease. I knew that for sure.

The pressure kept building, the walls kept caving in, I kept resisting. It all became so intense that it felt like my entire existence was about to explode. Maybe I'd never get back to earth and the life I was living.

Then it came to me. If that was how I'd really been living and unconsciously treating myself, then I didn't want to go back...

The moment that decision was made everything changed. The pressure dropped, the walls backed off, and the colours dimmed down. Music suddenly started playing and I heaved like I was going to be sick again. Instead of vomit it was gale force burps. Like negative energy once trapped deep in my body was finally being released. I followed it up with a huge scream that lasted three or four seconds.

I stood up and swayed a little from side to side, feeling dizzy and very weak. I'd made it and decades' worth of emotional garbage was finally disposed of. Jules opened the bathroom door and smiled at me.

"It's all over," he said. "It's gone." We hugged and then he led me back to the ceremony room and handed me a glass of water. Delilah looked drained. It was almost 1a.m. Six hours. Three cups. One mind-blowing, life-changing journey.

That second ceremony in the Netherlands was undoubtedly the most difficult experience of my life...yet at the same time the most rewarding and transformative. I'd no idea how badly I'd treated myself. No idea that by always trying to impress others, gain their attention and approval meant that I was neglecting myself. Completely oblivious to the truth that I was hurting me more than anyone else ever could by not accepting and loving myself.

We need to be kinder to ourselves. We need to become our own best friend. I think if we all paid closer attention to some of our inner talk we'd be pretty shocked. I was shown clearly that negative self-talk and self-loathing makes us sick. Mental torture can lead to physical disease, and it's tragic if we're doing that to ourselves.

You're loved and you deserve love. Be kind to yourself.

CHAPTER 17

≈

Choosing The Right Ayahuasca Retreat

With hundreds of ayahausca retreats based all over the world now, and many of them working in different ways, how do you know which one is right for you? How do you ensure you have the safest possible experience?

Ronald Weber, who was born in the Netherlands but has been living in Peru for four years, can hopefully answer those questions for you. He is vice president of the Ayahuasca Safety Association, which was formed in late 2016 by a group of five retreat owners.

Ayahuasca has now become a booming tourism industry in Peru, and the medicine has spread globally, even being used underground in some countries where it's classed as an illegal drug.

Promoting the safe and responsible use of the medicine is the number one aim of the Ayahuasca Safety Association. The organisation's members also have ambitions to introduce a set of ethical rules, medical rules, and safety rules that all ayahuasca retreats in Peru can collectively operate under.

In recent years, two deaths recorded at ayahuasca retreats hit the headlines and sparked a media frenzy where the brew was blamed. Neither of the deaths of those individuals were linked directly to the drinking of ayahuasca.

A British man was fatally stabbed by another ayahuasca drinker, while at another retreat a young from New Zealand tragically died after being poisoned by drinking the tobacco tea 'mapacho', sometimes used in preparation for an ayahuasca ceremony to clean or purge the body of toxins. Although Ronald is of the opinion that other safer purging methods exist which are preferable to the use of mapacho as a cleansing medicine in preparation for an ayahuasca ceremony. I won't go into any more detail on these sad events because there is plenty information on the internet about what happened.

However, the latter death in 2015 and the initial misrepresentation in the media prompted several retreat owners to form the Ayahuasca Safety Association. Ronald, who currently runs plant medicine ceremonies at the Ayahuasca Medicine House and other centres in Iquitos, a colleague from The Temple of the Way of Light centre, and a few other retreat owners held several meetings to discuss improving safety for everyone.

Ronald and the other founder members intend on developing the association and growing its membership. Their aim is for all centres to contribute to the creation of positive protocols that will help regulate what is largely an unregulated industry.

The stories in this book demonstrate the amazing healing power of ayahuasca, but it's not suitable for everyone. People currently taking certain medications, such as anti-depressants, are advised not to drink ayahuasca because of negative interactions with the brew. Others with certain illnesses, for example schizophrenia, are strongly recommended not to drink ayahuasca. High blood pressure is also a concern and people with diabetes type 1 should be carefully evaluated before being admitted to ceremonies.

If you're considering drinking ayahuasca for the first time, Ronald's responses to my questions below can help you prepare properly, choose the retreat that's right for you, and get the most from your ayahuasca experience.

For someone who wants to drink the medicine for the first time, what steps should they take to ensure they have the safest possible experience

First, inform themselves of what it actually is. On the internet there are a lot of stories which talk very positively about ayahuasca - which is absolutely true. But the negative part is that when you're drinking the medicine you are confronted with some dark parts of yourself. Those experiences can be hard, and sometimes I notice that people are not prepared for that.

Double check the details of the centre you work with. See if they have a tax number (called a RUC number in Peru) – because you can put that tax number into a tax authority search engine in Peru and look up where the company is located, when it was established, and who the legal representatives are.

When you are dealing with legitimate centres that are tax registered the chance that you'll have a negative experience already becomes very low because of the responsibility those centres have.

I would estimate that there are around 50 centres who are registered (for tax) in Peru and do declare their activities, and have a business practice and the necessary licenses needed to operate commercially required by Peruvian law.

Is it important to make people aware that there are some dangers with ayahuasca?

Yes absolutely. The first thing to check is if you are medically fit to actually drink ayahuasca. I have had people who have lied about their medication. What I always do before the ceremony is measure the blood pressure of a person who comes to drink with me for the first time.

The blood pressure tells me a lot about the person. The first time, of course, they are a little excited and the blood pressure rises. But if the blood pressure is too high you should decline them because there's a risk. If you do accept them you need to have a knowledge of how different kind of brews affect blood pressure.

In the summer of 2016, I bought a professional blood pressure meter which they use in hospitals. I began measuring blood pressure at Ayahuasca Medicine House before, during and after ceremony. I did that for three months with different people having three ceremonies in a row. With every person I discovered that when you change the ratio of the ayahuasca vine, which has the MAO inhibitors in it, and the leaves, which has the DMT in it, it can actually raise or lower the blood pressure.

Besides taking the blood pressure to determine if someone is in the safe zone, when you have a person who has a relatively low blood pressure you should not give them ayahuasca that is low with leaves and DMT content. These people fall asleep because the blood pressure will drop too low. These people should be given higher amounts of DMT to raise their blood pressure a little bit so they have an experience where don't fall asleep.

At the same time, you have to feel either intuitively or with pure logic, to determine the amount of the drink you give. Then you can optimise the amount and what kind of medicine you serve to a person. It is preferable to serve a smaller than usual cup size for the first time to see how they respond. If you serve them too much the first time, people can have a difficult experience and then they can have a stressed reaction which influences the experience negatively

It's also necessary that people are completely transparent about what type of ayahuasca they use and serve. I make all my ayahuasca brews myself and I label all my bottles with the production date, the source materials, and which batch number, so I know exactly what I'm giving to the person.

People can also check that on the bottle because there's a lot of centres over here that are using ayahuasca that's not coming from them, and they have no idea what's in it. Because of the demand of tourists over here to have a psychedelic experience - a lot of lights and colour - they add other plants to it which might be more dangerous than the original ayahuasca blend.

Who or what types of people should NOT drink ayahuasca?

I would be very cautious with people who have diabetes type 1. They have, from what I've learned, an unpredictable blood pressure response with ayahuasca. It's virtually impossible to predict that very well.

The second type of person is one who is on medication that is known to be incompatible with ayahuasca. From a pharmacy point of view there is a database on the internet, where you can look up the interactions between ayahuasca and monoamine oxidase inhibitor (MAOI, from the vine) and medications such as antidepressants or other modern drugs (A list of drugs and specific foods that are contraindicated with ayahuasca can be found via this article on the Multidisciplinary Association for Psychedelic Studies website: https://www.maps.org/news-letters/v06n1/06158mao.html).

I also do not recommend that people who are schizophrenic, or have a schizophrenic history, drink ayahuasca. I am also very careful with people who are now off medication but have a history one or two years ago where they were taking psychiatric medicines either in a mental institute or at home.

Taking these kinds of drugs does affect the brain chemistry, which can be further affected by ayahuasca. There are exceptional cases but when you help these people you have to be careful what kind of ayahuasca you serve them, what kind of dose, and they need very specific personal attention.

I was under the impression that if you were off anti-depressants for six weeks or longer you could go through a ceremony. What's your position on that?

In general, that is true. But there's also a personal evaluation because if you are off meds it doesn't mean you are cured of the illness. You may be dealing with someone who has bipolar disorder and has not taken medication for a year or so, and at first seems stable, but before that had a history of taking very heavy psychiatric drugs which, in my view, cause damage to the brain.

They may appear stable and feel this way within themselves, but when they drink ayahuasca and the amount is too much, these issues which are not processed can come to the surface in ceremony and sometimes be aggressive.

There is a responsibility on the part of the people who drink ayahuasca to inform themselves and be honest with themselves that they're at least medically compatible. They also have to be honest communicating medical issues with people at the centres they are planning to go to.

On three occasions, right before ceremony, I have given money back to people and said, "I'm sorry but I cannot allow you to drink for your safety, but also for the safety of the others".

This may look like I'm painting a black picture. I'm not, I'm only highlighting some dangers and being responsible. The amount of good that comes from drinking ayahuasca is far, far more greater than the smaller incidences I'm talking about now.

Do you think it's a good thing that ayahuasca is spreading far beyond the Amazon? What are the pros and cons of this?

The pros of this is that some people who can really benefit from drinking ayahuasca do not have access to this kind of medicine because it is not available or illegal in their country. It can do wonders - but it's not a magic bullet.

It can provoke very profound changes in the lives of people, which can be very positive. If you take the right precautions, do the right screening, and preparations, the risk of harm from drinking ayahuasca is very minimal.

But there is cost involved, and unfortunately there are some people operating in countries worldwide who are just interested in the money. That's the con side.

A facilitator may think, 'the ayahuasca costs so much, accommodation costs so much, food costs so much…that's a 400 percent profit margin, let's do that'. They are not principally interested in curing people.

For cost and accessibility reasons many people choose to drink ayahuasca at retreats in Europe. Do you think the centres in Europe overall can do just as good a job as those in the Amazon led by shamans?

Peru should be someone's first choice if they can afford it. You cannot compare an authentic, true-hearted curandero holding a ceremony here in the jungle with some people who have drunk, let's say 10 times or even hundreds of times, and run ceremonies in Europe.

It makes a difference what kind of setting - the environment you are in - whether that's the jungle or the city. If you drink in these other places, as I have in the past, you have a completely different experience.

I'm of the opinion that you should preferably drink ayahuasca in the jungle. San Pedro or wachuma, the cactus, you should preferably drink in the mountains where it's originated from.

Of course you can drink in Europe and the United States aswell, and there are many people who know absolutely what they are doing and have a certain amount of training and experience.

Here in Peru, if you walk along the street and meet a person who says, "I am a maestro in plant medicines, and I can do this and that..." then you should actually turn around and walk very fast in the other direction. All the true masters I've met over here are very humble and common.

They blend in and when you meet them on the streets you have no idea that these people are actually are so advanced in working with plant medicines because they don't need to prove themselves.

What advice do you have for people to properly integrate their ayahuasca experiences when they return home and go on with their daily lives?

The most important thing is that after your last ceremony you should take care of your diet. For at least three days after your last consumption of ayahuasca you shouldn't drink alcohol, and also stay away from pork meat for at least two weeks. For pork meat there are cultural and traditional reasons, and people say it is not a clean animal. People can also have a strong reaction in their digestive system.

Do not immediately return to the internet, or read all the news of the day. No, instead connect with yourself. For me, the ceremony is not the most important thing any more. It is the day after when you have come down to earth and have time to rethink the experiences, go over your thoughts and the feelings you had during the ceremony.

What's the use of coming over here, drinking ayahuasca, seeing lots of lights and colours, and then not really learn anything about the experience? Do it the right way, with no alcohol, a clean diet and rhythm for a couple of weeks. Give the medicine the maximum opportunity to integrate with your body, mind and soul.

People who do this have the most profound and beneficial effects. For people who have been addicted to all sorts of drugs, it's fairly common for the medicine to have them disconnected from their drug addiction.

What's crucial is that when these people return home they absolutely should change something profound within their daily life.

That could mean moving to another town, looking for new friends, getting rid of old friends, searching for a new job, or a new hobby. Because if they return to their normal life then it's only a matter of time before they will fall back into their addiction. I've seen that more than once. Sometimes it can mean making big decisions like breaking relationships after realising that they're not good for them.

Some people experience 'the calling', while some don't. How does someone know if ayahuasca is right for them?

I would only say ayahuasca is right for you if you do feel it inside - but don't have expectations. You can have intentions, but expectations never come out the way you think they should. Ayahausca gives you what you need and not what you want.

I have many people who come here at a point in their life where they don't know what to do anymore. They expect to sit back, relax, and the answers will come through ayahuasca. It doesn't work that way. Ayahuasca doesn't tell you what to do because, with the universal law of free will, you have the responsibility to make the end decision.

What you can do, during the influence of ayahuasca, is just visualise situations and then feel how that feels for you. That gives you much more reality about the success of the situation because at the end it's you who will make the decision.

****

Joeri Oomen, whose story was featured in chapter 13, and his team at Ayamundo have been promoting the responsible drinking of ayahuasca in a safe setting for years.

In 2017, the Ayamundo guys visited the Ayahuasca Safety Association in Iquitos and also spoke with Ronald about minimising risks for ayahuasca drinkers and helping people get the best experience possible.

Afterwards, Ayamundo created a 12 point checklist to assist people who are considering drinking ayahuasca. It includes some important considerations and key questions people can ask to determine whether or not they want to use a particular retreat.

Some of these points are specific only to retreats in the Amazon, however some considerations such as numbers 8, 9, and 10 are important no matter where in the world you may drink ayahuasca.

12 Point Checklist For Choosing The Right Ayahuasca Retreat

1. **Find out what protocols the centre has in case any accidents occur.** This is especially important for Peru where many centres are in

the jungle. How long does it take to get to the nearest hospital? Does the retreat have its own transportation?

2. **Is there a medical kit on site - and what's in it?** A retreat in the Amazon has the danger of snake bites, therefore having anti-venom on site could be life-saving. On the other hand, a centre may only treat any sickness with their traditional plant medicines found in the jungle. It is up to you to make the decision.

3. **Is there any phone communication with the nearest city?** Again, this is important in the case of isolated retreats in the Amazonian jungle.

4. **Is there someone with a first aid certificate at the retreat?**

5. **Find out what shamans are working at the centre and what experience they have in working with the medicine.**

6. **Be careful if a shaman is touchy or tries to guide you away from the group**. Ask a guide to go with you. In Peru personal space is defined differently from other countries. While it is rare, some shamans have abused their position.

7. **Find out what ingredients are being used in the ayahuasca.** Shamans largely use two ingredients: the ayahuasca vine and chacruna leaves. However, some add other ingredients which may be toxic if too much is used. In European countries a combination of the ayahuasca vine/mimosa or harmala/mimosa is more common.

8. **The ayahuasca centre should do a medical screening with questionnaire.** Some centres also have medical expertise and this is worth investigating.

9. **Always be honest about medication you use in your medical screening.** Some may interact badly with the ayahuasca medicine and cause problems.

10. **How many of the retreat's leaders and guides drink ayahuasca?** There should always be at least one person sober so they can make a good judgement on the situation during ceremonies.

11. **After the ceremony will you be guided to your hut, or will there be a sitter?** Sometimes the maloka - the ceremonial space in South America - is near to the hut you're sleeping in and easy for facilitators to guide you there. However, some can be a couple of hundred metres away in the jungle and difficult to find in the darkness.

12. **Do research in advance and read reviews on various websites.** Be cautious that some reviews online can be fake, which is why Ayamundo makes it possible for you to contact the people who write reviews.

CONCLUSION

Sixteen individuals. Eight different nationalities. All of them with one thing in common…

Ayahuasca came into their lives when they needed it most - and transformed their world.

When I began tracking down people to interview for this book, what I wanted to find were the strongest examples of lives being positively turned around. People who had gone from suffering and struggling in life to feeling reborn, revitalised, and ultimately like a brand new person after drinking ayahuasca.

This is what it felt like for me, and I knew there were countless more out there. In writing this book, I wanted to focus less on the psychedelic effects, the colour, and the drama of ayahuasca, and more on the positive outcomes people had. Inspiring stories that would give others hope.

I interviewed these people over the phone over the course of four months - and loved every second of hearing how they'd overcome their darkest days through ayahuasca. There's something exciting and inspiring about tales of other human beings pulling through in the end. Especially when they've gone through tough times you can relate to.

These people completely opened up about sexual abuse, PTSD, depression, eating disorders, disabilities and more. Some were on the brink of suicide. All of them felt lost.

Yet they found a way to find themselves. When drugs, therapy, and every other method of healing they tried had failed, the Amazonian plant medicine worked like magic. Ayahuasca's certainly not for everyone, but could it be for you?

While I was riding high on the wave of the ayahuasca aftermath for months, I discovered that the real work continued over the next year. I found myself in very similar problematic situations as before. They were difficult but I felt as if I was being tested in order to make better decisions from a different level of self-awareness.

It's clear that ayahuasca shines a light on where we've been going wrong in life, but it's then down to us to make the appropriate adjustments in our everyday lives afterwards.

"With ayahuasca, she'll show you what you need to do - but really you have to put in the effort afterwards. The ceremony is the easy part." - Veronika Poola, chapter 14.

A few months after my first retreat, I returned to the Netherlands for another ayahuasca ceremony. This was followed by a psychedelic experience with psilocybin mushrooms, both of which helped me heal my relationship with my father.

It gave me a different perspective on the past, along with the courage to speak with my dad about him leaving when I was a young boy. The dreaded chat we'd both avoided for decades, thinking it'd be much easier to leave the sticking plaster on old wounds.

That Sunday morning on August 6th, 2017, we finally spoke openly and I saw my dad cry for the first time. It might well be the most important conversation I've ever had - because my dad died four months later. Maybe I'll share what was said another day.

But on interviewing the others in this book, it became clear that our childhood experiences are at the root of our problems as adults. We all carry emotional baggage to some degree from our youth. It's just part of being human and trying to cope with living in this world.

"You 100% have to deal with the family stuff first. It's usually dealing with mum, dad, or significant events that happened as a child because patterns are created that become bigger and bigger." - Anna Keppen, chapter 5.

For some people, the baggage becomes too heavy and, if we take responsibility for our own situations, we can lighten the load.

What if you could turn back the clock? What if you could blast open your subconscious mind and really understand what's going on? What if you could hit the 'reset' button and break the destructive patterns that only lead to unhappiness?

"With ayahuasca you are your own therapist and you come into dimensions within yourself that you could never reach just by talking. It shows you so clearly what you do with your thoughts, emotions and your behaviour." - Nicolette Van der Waal, chapter 9.

Ayahuasca is not a cure all and it's not suitable for everyone. It can be dangerous in the wrong hands and when not used properly. If you're considering drinking the medicine then please read over the 12 point checklist in the previous pages, and follow the advice given in the interview by Ronald Weber, vice president of the Ayahuasca Safety Association.

I do believe, however, that plant medicines like ayahuasca are here help us heal - and for us to grow to new levels of consciousness. In Western society, we largely rely on drugs and pharmaceutical companies to try and maintain health, yet we're becoming sicker and sicker. We mask symptoms and don't tackle the root cause. We don't properly heal.

But there's a global shift happening. The medicine is spreading, just like a vine, throughout the world and more people are waking up. Becoming more and more of who they actually are.

All through The Healing Power of Ayahuasca.

I hope you've enjoyed reading this book, and would really appreciate it if you posted a review on the Amazon website. I'd also love to hear your feedback on the book, and if you connected with any particular story. Feel free to email me: **marc@healingpowerofaya.com**

All the best, Marc

Free Audio Download For You

Hear the first-hand accounts of 10 of the people interviewed in this book as they talk about their magical experiences with ayahuasca.

Author Marc McLean has pulled together snippets from the recorded interviews he did with the men and women sharing their stories in *The Healing Power Of Ayahuasca.*

Hear their voices as they speak openly about their ayahuasca journeys, their biggest lessons they learned from drinking the plant medicine, and their advice for readers like you.

You can download the audio recording online by visiting: www.healingpowerofaya.com/audio

The Healing Power Of Ayahuasca

16 Incredible Life Transformations That Will Inspire Your Self-Discovery

Thanks

At the beginning of 2018 my friends, Alan and Paul, encouraged me to write a book about ayahuasca. At that point I had no book title in mind, no other stories apart from my own, and no proper idea of what shape this book would take.

I only knew I wanted to interview other people from around the world about their own personal healing journeys, and share their stories with others. After I put the word out into ayahuasca circles, everything fell into place. One person after another contacted me, and each time I was blown away by what they told me ayahuasca had done for them. The book began to develop organically as each month passed and I made new friends along the way.

So, for their contributions, I'd like to thank Ciaran, Fred, Annette, Anna, Stephen, Scott, Finola, Nicolette, Gohar, James, Kent, Bernardine, Joeri, Veronika, Felipe, and Ronald. You've all been honest and completely open about some of the toughest times in your life, and I'm certain your stories will inspire other people to overcome theirs too.

A huge thanks also to my mum, Victoria, Paul, Alan, my friend and editor Ian Baillie, and to Jules and Delilah for all their love and support.

About The Author

Marc McLean's writing career began as a journalist at his local newspaper in West Dunbartonshire, Scotland, in 2001.

He spent more than 15 years working in the media, and also went onto become a fitness coach.

Marc has also published a series of books focusing on strength training and good nutrition.

His hobbies include hillwalking, cycling, travelling, enjoying the outdoors, strength training, playing poker, and reading.

You can contact Marc here:

Email: marc@healingpowerofaya.com
Website: www.healingpowerofaya.com

Made in the USA
Columbia, SC
19 February 2019